GREEN UNIVERSE

Also by Edward F. Dolan, Jr.

Pasteur and the Invisible Giants

GREEN UNIVERSE

THE STORY OF

Alexander von Humboldt

By

EDWARD F. DOLAN, Jr.

DODD, MEAD & COMPANY

NEW YORK

Library of Congress Catalog Card Number: 59-12739

Printed in the United States of America
by The Cornwall Press, Inc., Cornwall, N. Y.

This is for my father, Edward F. Dolan, Sr.,
and his father, George J. Dolan, Sr.
I remember them as gentle men.

Contents

GREEN UNIVERSE

CHAPTER ONE

A Ship Sails

Suddenly, the young man wanted to laugh.

He had spent the past ten minutes roaming the entire length of the ship's deck, from the high, narrow stern to the unpainted mainmast and then to the bowsprit with its jibs snapping angrily against a stiff wind, and back again. He had sent his gaze darting in all directions to view an array of sights strange to his landsman's eyes. Overhead, brown-faced seamen had scurried, monkeylike, up fraying ratlines to let down a topgallant that had at last unfurled with a long, sighing roar. The Spanish flag had been run up to the crown of the mizzen. Captain Hernando Rodriquez, his feet planted wide apart on his quarterdeck, had bellowed, one after the other, orders that only a sailor could understand. Amidships, leathery hands had deftly lashed ropes about belaying cleats.

The laugh escaped his lips. In his excitement he had been trying to record for memory all that was happening aboard the frigate *Pizarro* as it sailed out of the harbor of La

Coruña at the northern tip of Spain. But it was not humanly possible to see *everything* at once. He would probably not remember clearly a single thing that came into view.

And so, abruptly slowing his steps, he walked to the port rail and gripped it firmly. The wood was rough and damp against his palms. Breathing deeply of the salt air sweeping in under gray, sullen clouds from the harbor entrance, he ordered his nerves to quiet themselves. He told himself he must remember each and every sight and sound of this, the most important day of his life—the day of June 5, 1799, when he, Alexander von Humboldt, put Europe behind him and began the westward journey to the jungles and muddy rivers and disease-laden heat of South America.

He was a young man whose appearance could be confusing, this twenty-nine-year-old Baron von Humboldt of Germany. He was of medium height and slender build; but his heavy greatcoat, skin-tight white breeches, black polished boots, and high crowned hat added inches and pounds to his figure. A long, boney nose and high forehead, the latter etched with smallpox scars, made the upper part of his face seem narrow, while full lips and a prominent, rounded chin gave the lower area of that face an appearance of thickness and wideness. With somber gray eyes and dark hair curving fashionably over his ears to the base of his neck, he impressed one as a quiet man of bookish tastes—perhaps a teacher or a librarian, perhaps nothing more than an idle but well-educated aristocrat.

But the truth of the matter was that he was a highly trained geologist, afire since childhood to the very core of his being with the desire to travel; to finger rocks and plants and chunks of earth that no European had ever touched; to climb mountains that no European had climbed; and clamber down into volcanoes that no European—or any other man in his right mind, for that matter—would dream of entering.

Humboldt looked boyish and eager now as he studied the passing shoreline of La Coruña with its streaked white walls and dull red roofs, and he could not restrain himself from murmuring a little foolishly to himself, "Good-bye, La Coruña. No more putting up with your stench and your narrow streets and your bad food." His eyes swept upward to the magnificent mountains behind the town and his mind embraced all the mountains, plains, and valleys stretching away for thousands of miles behind them. "And farewell, Europe. No more eating my heart out because I cannot do the work I love. No more planning expeditions that never begin. No more waiting for ships that will not—cannot—sail because the mighty Napoleon is on the march."

His gaze turned to the harbor entrance. He caught his first view of the restless Atlantic swells. "And hail to whatever is beyond that gray horizon." Hail to his destination, Cuba, and to all the mysterious lands ringing it—Mexico, New Granada, Panama, the Captaincy General of Venezuela, Peru, and the growing United States. Mysterious lands to him now. But later, no. No indeed!

Bare feet pattered along the deck to his side. A sailor, naked to the waist in spite of the cold, saluted with the almost arrogant casualness that men of the sea reserve for those of the land. Alexander straightened, embarrassed to be caught mumbling idiotically to himself, and, with what he hoped was a frown of dignity, heard the man say, "The Captain desires to speak with you, Señor."

Alexander nodded and thanked the man in Spanish; he spoke not only the tongue of the *Pizarro,* but English and French, as well as his own native German. He moved aft to the quarterdeck. Captain Hernando Rodriquez stood with his helmsman at the wheel, ordering periodic changes in course in an effort to pick up a favorable wind.

"You wished to speak with me, Captain?"

"Yes." Rodriquez did not merely speak the word; he snapped it. He ordered the helmsman onto a new tack and stepped away from the wheel. Alexander found his every movement and gesture terse and angry, undoubtedly the result of a lifetime spent keeping tiny ships afloat on the temperamental Atlantic. Like so many of his men, Rodriquez was short, dark haired, bearded, and narrow faced. Poor diet had rotted his teeth. Sun and rain and wind bristling with salt had made his skin as tough as an animal's hide. His uniform, once splendid with its bright buttons and outsized epaulets, was now stained and worn thin from too many years at sea.

Rodriquez led the way to the starboard side of the stern rail. There, piled high on the deck and covered with a tarpaulin, were the crates containing the scientific gear Alexander was carrying to the New World: the hygrometers of Deluc and Saussure for measuring humidity; electrometers for detecting electricity in the air; barometers, thermometers, the wonderful sextant from London; surveying equipment, paraphernalia for fishing, insect hunting, and plant collecting; current maps and navigational charts, and rolls of thick paper on which new and more accurate maps and charts would be drawn. Hovering over all this neatly packaged material was Aimé Bonpland, the giant Frenchman who was to be Alexander's partner in this New World adventure.

Rodriquez halted, placing himself between Bonpland and Alexander. Setting his feet wide apart and clasping his hands behind his back in the characteristic stance of a seaman aboard a rolling ship, he said, "I want to warn you again."

Aimé, standing just behind the Captain's shoulder and towering above him like an amiable mountain, lifted exasperated eyes skyward. Rodriquez had been "warning" them constantly since that moment yesterday when the bad news had come through from the watchtower at Sisarga. Now he was going to deliver his little speech all over again.

"I just want to caution you against building too high your hopes of seeing the New World. We may never lose sight of Europe."

"I know—" Alexander began.

"The watchtower reported that the British squadron has three frigates standing to the south off the Tagus River. If they sight us, I will do my best to outrun them."

"And we trust you'll be successful, Captain," Aimé said. His voice, befitting a man of his size, was deep and rumbling.

"But it is more likely that I'll *not* be successful," Rodriquez snapped. "She is a good ship, this old *Pizarro,* but she is not fast. If the British catch us, we will be made prisoners and it will be internment in Portugal for us. And your valuable equipment will be confiscated. You must not blame me if that happens."

"I assure you, we won't blame you. And in the meantime, we shall hold every confidence in your ability to outrun and outwit the British," Alexander said. He spoke with more formality than was necessary, in an effort to control his impatience. The *Pizarro* was now running past the jagged rocks that lined the northwestern rim of the harbor. The bulky shadow of Fort San Amarro seemed to reach out for the ship, and, over the stern, that sprawling mass of granite called the Castle of San Antonio dominated all La Coruña. Alexander did not want to squander these precious minutes listening to a fretting Captain and thinking of the three British ships. In particular, he did not want to think of the British ships.

Rodriquez must have sensed his mood, for abruptly he shrugged and said, "I merely wanted you to know my feelings," and stalked back to the wheel.

Left alone, Alexander and Aimé descended to the main deck and peered out toward the harbor entrance. Aimé, four years Alexander's junior, put his elbows on the rail and hunched his shoulders. He was wearing a faded blue topcoat, shredding at the cuffs and showing several moth holes. His face, not unlike a lumpy moon, was mottled with the cold. His hair, very dark, was so thick and tousled that Alexander often thought that the term "barber's shears" was not in Aimé's vocabulary. Ordinarily, the Frenchman was quick to smile; but now his bushy eyebrows were angled down over the bridge of his nose in a frown. "It's bad luck—this thing about the British ships."

"Yes. But what else could we expect?" Ever since the Spanish, led by that so-called "Prince of Peace," Prime Minister Manuel de Godoy, had joined Napoleon in making war on England, British ships had blockaded the ports of Spain in a move to destroy that country's ocean commerce, a move proving highly successful. "We were bound to run into trouble of this sort."

Aimé stared at his big, knotted hands. The wind blew thick strands of dark hair across his forehead. Suddenly, he pounded the rail. "*Napoleon!* I hate the very sound of his name. He is the curse of the world!"

"He's our curse, at least," Alexander agreed with grim amusement.

Aimé returned his eyes to the harbor entrance. Like Alexander, he had waited for this first moment of travel all his life. "They must not sight us. Those British must not sight us." The words, coming so softly after a moment of harsh anger, had about them the quality of a prayer.

"We must not even think of them."

"But that's impossible."

"Perhaps. But necessary. Did you ever play hiding games when you were a boy?"

The Frenchman stared at Alexander as though his friend had taken leave of his senses. "Of course. But what does that have to do with the British?"

"Everything." Alexander leaned against the rail and studied the water curling away from under the ship. "I remember how I would hide in the bushes and my brother, Wilhelm, would come looking for me. Sometimes he would stop just a few feet from my hiding place. If I began to think: 'Don't look this way, don't look this way,' he was sure to turn right to me. It was as if he had sensed my very thoughts. But if I would think of nothing at all or of other things—even something silly like, 'My, what a pretty day this is,' he would often walk away without glancing in my direction. Maybe the same thing would work now with the British."

Aimé threw back his great head and laughed a roaring laugh. "All right, my friend. I've had exactly the same experience. Perhaps all children have. So we will think of other things." He brought a hand down affectionately on the shoulder of the man who, in little more than a year, had come to mean as much to him as a brother. He made a game of their conversation. "We will think of the New World. I wonder what it holds for us?"

Alexander could only guess at the answers. There would be work, of course. And adventure. And hardship.

But what else? Only time would tell.

For Aimé, there would be renown as a botanist. With Humboldt, he would collect some 60,000 South American plant specimens and describe approximately 3,500 new species. And later, for Aimé, there would be tragedy.

For Alexander, there would be lasting fame in no less than ten fields of scientific endeavor—anthropology, astronomy, botany, geography, geology, geophysics, meteorology, oceanography, physiology, and zoology. And he would be known, too, as a humanitarian, a statesman, a philosopher, and an author.

But all this lay in the future for the young explorer-scientists as the *Pizarro* moved out of La Coruña. Humboldt had fallen silent at the rail, and Aimé Bonpland, guessing his thoughts, said, "I understood we weren't to think about the British."

Alexander shrugged, smiling. "I wasn't thinking of the British as much as I was of Napoleon." For a moment, he studied quietly the water foaming below him. "I don't understand it. I've wanted to do one thing all my life—explore. It seems to me that someone has always tried to get in the way of that ambition. First, it was my mother. Now, it's Napoleon."

More than a year ago, Alexander had finally escaped his family and had set out to follow his star as an explorer. All during that time, the shadow of Napoleon had haunted him. That dumpy, posturing Corsican, that dictator rising up from the blood-red wake of what had been intended as a nation's revolt against tyranny, that former corporal now out to conquer the world had balked every one of his attempts to sail out from Europe.

First, there had been the Baudin disappointment. Shortly after his arrival in Paris, Alexander had been selected to accompany Captain Charles Baudin on a voyage around the world. That expedition had been postponed—for a year, at least—on orders from Bonaparte.

Next had come an offer from the Britisher, Lord Frederick

Bristol, to travel with him to Egypt to study the antiquities found along the Upper Nile. But, again, the shadow of Napoleon. Bristol, on a visit to Italy, was shackled and deposited in prison. Bonaparte was planning an expedition of his own, a military one, into Egypt and wanted no Englishman snooping about in the vicinity.

Then, in the autumn of 1798, the Corsican himself had given Alexander the chance to travel. After conquering most of Egypt, he had decided to become a patron of science and had ordered that an expedition of 160 scientists, among them that German fellow, Humboldt, be formed to follow the French legions along the Nile to collect and codify the wonders found there. Down to Marseille went Alexander, only to learn that a sailing to Algiers was out of the question because the one-eyed, one-armed Admiral Horatio Nelson had thoroughly trounced the French fleet at Aboukir and had set up a blockade across the Mediterranean Sea and up the Atlantic.

Alexander could thank Napoleon for one thing, though—his friendship with Aimé Bonpland, medical doctor by profession, botanist by love and ambition, vigorous and happy child by nature. Aimé also was to have gone to Egypt, and the two young men found themselves thrown together at Marseille. They spent the empty days listening quietly and comfortingly to each other's words of disappointment. They came to know each other well. They learned that each had been born with the quenchless fire of travel in him. Before they were done with Marseille, out of blasted hopes there had emerged a friendship that time could not break, and they heard themselves saying excitedly, "We must remain together. We make a fine team for scientific exploration—one to study the plant life of a country, the other its geography and geology." The more they thought of themselves moving together through strange lands, the better they liked the idea. They sealed with a handshake a partnership that was to endure for more than fifteen years.

But where first to travel as a team? Egypt was out of the question. "But there's still the rest of the world to see," they had said. "The South Pacific. China. Russia. The United States. The countries of South America—Peru, Ecuador, Venezuela . . ."

South America.

The name of that continent lingered, hauntingly and invitingly, on their lips. Explore South America together. Why not? That vast, wild land was ripe for investigation. Christopher Columbus had led the way there. The Spanish and Portuguese had conquered it and had tried to wring its earth dry of gold. Jesuits and Capuchins and Franciscans had brought Christianity to the natives. Charles Marie La Condamine and Pierre Bouguer and José Celestino Mutis had broken the ground for scientific exploration, and now the country was ready for just such an exploration.

Just a fraction of all its plant and animal life and geologic record had been collected and codified. A truly dependable map of its coast, its jungles and savannahs, its countless rivers and its growing settlements, was yet to be drawn. A veil of mystery and legend continued to shroud the civilizations the first explorers had found there. Every returning voyager added to the rumor that the giant Orinoco and Amazon systems were connected, making an area nine times the size of the kingdom of Spain navigable by river. But no one as yet had pinpointed the exact location of that connection.

South America.

Yes, that was the place for them.

And so, together, they had crossed over into Spain and had presented their plan for a scientific exploration of South America to Foreign Minister Mariano Luis de Urquijo at Madrid. Through his good offices, they had secured the permission of King Charles IV to explore his New World provinces. To this, the monarch had added a letter directing all provincial officials, from governors to the commanders of the smallest garrisons, to assist in every manner possible the travels and studies of Baron von Humboldt and his companion, Citizen Aimé Bonpland of Paris. The officials of Spain shook their heads in amazement. Never had foreigners been granted such a sweeping visa.

Now, in mid-1799, here they were, standing on the deck of the *Pizarro* and feeling the rise and fall of the ship as it headed into the Atlantic, bearing a cargo of ambitious dreams.

The *Pizarro* sailed northwest until the land was hazy and low over the stern. Then it swung south for the run past Portugal and the three British frigates, toward its first stop, the Canary Islands.

CHAPTER TWO

The Invisible Harmony

THEIR LUCK WAS HOLDING as they approached their first port of call in the Canary Islands. Only once had they sighted British ships, but so far off to the southwest as to offer no threat to their passage. Each morning, at the sight of the empty horizon, Alexander and Aimé felt their spirits and hopes rise a little higher.

Not so Captain Hernando Rodriquez. Each day brought substantially the same pessimistic words from his lips. "They will yet appear, those British, sipping their tea and looking down their long noses at my little ship. We're not free of Europe yet. And, if it isn't the British, it will be something else. For that is the way of the sea."

"Nonsense!" Aimé had cried on their second morning out. "We're really on our way at last. I feel as if I'm alive for the first time in my life. No one can stop us now. Not all the Napoleons and Admiral Nelsons in creation!"

After that, the explorer-scientists paid the Captain's gray attitude no heed. Now was not the time for pessimism, they told themselves. Now was the time for work. Off and into trunks below decks went their good clothes, and on came the lightweight, open-throated shirts, tough breeches, and thick-soled boots that would serve as their everyday costumes for the next few years.

Yanking the tarpaulin from their square mountain of supplies, they got down to the daily work of explorers. They passed the entire voyage at the stern rail, sailing through fog and burning sun, through tranquil seas and then hard-running currents, and through nights so clear that they experienced no difficulty at all in reading the magnificent London-made sextant by moonlight.

Daily, they shot the sun to check the *Pizarro's* position, recorded the ocean's temperature, gauged the speed of currents, and hauled buckets of sea water aboard for a study of its chemical content.

On the sixth day out, when they were standing south of Portugal, they became hunters of the strange creatures living in that part of the Atlantic. Overside went lines and nets. The *Pizarro's* passengers, thirty souls from such widely separated countries as Austria and Guinea, gathered at the rail, chattering and sometimes screaming at the sight of the things brought inboard—things sometimes lifeless and foul smelling, or wiggling and spewing water all over the deck.

Off Gibraltar, there were jellyfish, called *Medusa,* that caused the explorers to jab each other excitedly.

"This is *Medusa aurita* of Baster. I'm sure of it."

"And isn't this *Medusa pelagia* of Bosc? See, Alex, it has the customary eight tentacles, all of them longer than the body."

The passengers did not take to that latter creature of the deep. That very night, Alexander placed it in a pewter plate. Then he struck the plate with a little metal bar.

There was a sharp, clanging noise and—wonder of wonders—the creature glowed for an instant like a candle. A ghostly, flickering candle. Which was quite enough for the three Negro passengers from Guinea, who fled to their cabin. They wanted no part of Black Magic. And Black Magic this surely was.

Even the smallest incident, as the days passed, had the flavor of adventure to it for the novice explorers. When the *Pizarro* stood between the coast of North Africa and the island of Madeira, a swallow came to rest on the topsail yard. Alexander immediately sent sailors up to fetch it—a simple task, for the tiny bird was too tired to move.

Then the explorer dashed to Captain Rodriquez on the quarterdeck.

"How far are we off Madeira, Captain?"

"Forty leagues, Señor."

"Are you certain?"

"Of course. We checked our course together this morning."

At that, Alexander turned in a full circle on the quarterdeck, his head flung far back as he stared at the crowns of the masts and the sky beyond. "There's just enough wind to keep us moving. And yet that bird, which could come from nowhere but Madeira, flew forty leagues. Without a good breeze to help it along. It's amazing!"

They came upon an even more amazing sight several days later. The *Pizarro,* on her fourteenth day out, had entered the area of the Canary Islands just beyond the islands of Losbos and Lancerata, and was heading for the city of Santa Cruz on the island of Tenerife, where she was to make port. Alexander sighted a log floating past the starboard side; grabbing Aimé's arm, he dragged him to the rail.

"Look at that! And I mean take a *very* close look at it. It's come all the way from the New World!"

Aimé, accustomed by now to his friend's outbursts, simply nodded, as if his friend's observation was one of the most sensible he had ever heard.

"It's an American cedar, Aimé. Look at the number of lichens covering it. The sea probably ripped it up from the New World coast and set it adrift. Ocean currents have carried it to this very spot. It will undoubtedly go ashore at Tenerife, but, had it been carried a little further south, it probably would have made the whole tour of the Atlantic and returned to its native soil with the general current of the tropics."

Alexander gazed happily at it as the passengers clustered about him. Always inspired by an audience, he had another thought. "Ocean currents. What a part they have played in the history of mankind, Aimé. They gave Columbus one of the many clues that finally led him to the New World. Do you know the story of the corpses and the bamboos of the Azores? No! Well, you shall hear it now."

He proceeded to relate a most fantastic tale. Toward the end of the fifteenth century, two corpses, the features of which indicated an unknown race of men, were cast up on the Azores. Shortly thereafter, the governor of Porto Santa—who happened to be the brother-in-law of Columbus—came upon large pieces of bamboo washed up on that island. When the corpses and the bamboo were shown to the Genoese navigator, he reasoned that both had been carried by ocean currents to the Azores from some distant shore, and his conviction of lands to the far west was further strengthened.

Such stories no longer surprised Aimé; he had been around Alexander too long for that. But the tale both astonished and amused the passengers. They really did not believe a word this Baron von Humboldt said, but he had made the voyage so very entertaining.

The only man aboard not entertained by him was Captain Rodriquez, who watched the group from his quarterdeck. To him, the explorer was a mystery, a mystery that deepened whenever he saw him kneeling over some dead sea creature on the deck, his hands covered with green slime; whenever he saw the man sit down to a meal without a single complaint about the rough sea fare or retire to his quarters without commenting bitterly on the stifling heat below decks; whenever he glimpsed him laughing into the wind, his clothes dripping and sea spray running off his long nose; and, particularly, whenever he thought of the wild, hard, cruel land in which the German would spend the next—and maybe last—years of his life.

Trying to solve the mystery, the Captain had watched closely and listened intently to Alexander all during the voyage. But all the things he saw and heard merely intensified his bewilderment. Direct conversation—that was what was required if he were to have his solution. He chose the final night of the first leg of the voyage for that conversation. As the *Pizarro,* all lights extinguished to conceal itself from any lurking English vessels, was sliding toward the harbor of Santa Cruz, Rodriquez approached Alexander and Aimé at their usual place at the stern rail. Alexander was seated on one of the supply crates. The Captain strode directly to him and then stood, shifting uncomfortably from one foot to the other while trying to think of a way to get to what was on his mind.

At last, he began, rather lamely, "It's a fine night."

"Yes."

"But we could use some fog. Anything to hide us from the British—if they're in these waters."

"Perhaps it will come before morning."

"Yes. Perhaps." Rodriquez cleared his throat. He clasped his hands behind his back. He glared up at the mizzen, an unearthly gray in the moonlight. Hang it! He was not a subtle man. There was no indirect way to find out what he wanted to know about this man. His eyes came down hard on Alexander's face and he heard himself snap when he really did not want to snap, "You must come from a fine home."

The explorer's brows arched. Was this a question or a statement of fact? Then came the polite but bewildered reply. "Yes. A very beautiful home."

"It has gardens?"

"Yes. And woods."

"And big rooms?"

Now Alexander was smiling, still puzzled, but enjoying the strange line the talk was taking. "Very big, as I remember them."

"You would say, then, that your home was very comfortable?"

"I would."

Rodriquez nodded. He snorted with satisfaction, slapping his hands together behind his back. He stared at Alexander with the same fierce expression he reserved for some seaman derelict in his duty. "Then why on earth did you leave it? Why are you willing to endure hardships and loneliness when you could be so comfortable in your fine home? Why do you travel?"

A smile of understanding lighted Alexander's face. What was troubling the Captain was out at last. The smile turned into an expression of thoughtfulness and then into one of helplessness. He shrugged. "I travel because it is my life."

"It's all you have ever wanted to do?"

"Yes."

"You haven't wanted to put your roots down somewhere and raise a family, like most other men?"

"Truthfully, no."

"You have wanted only to travel?"

"Yes."

"But what sort of a life is *that* for a man of your upbringing? For any man, for that matter? You could stay home. You could be a power in your country. You could be anything you wanted to be."

Again Alexander shrugged. And just as helplessly. "But I just want to travel. I think it is a good life. And I *know* it is the life for me." He came to his feet. He stood very close to Rodriquez. "Why do you ask me these questions, Captain? You, too, travel. You have spent your life at it. Surely you must know how I feel."

"With me, it is different," Rodriquez said. "I am a traveler, a seaman, because my father and grandfather and his father before him were seamen. It was the only thing I was ever taught to be. I am at sea not because I love it, but because I have to be."

"We are the same, Captain. With but one exception. I love my work. But I also travel because I *have* to. It was born in me and there is nothing I can do about it."

He turned slowly and moved to the stern rail. He stared, silent and thoughtful, at a mist coming in low over the sea.

This love of travel; this compulsion to roam the face of the earth; this inability to settle in one spot and say, "Here I will build my home and here I will raise my family and from here I shall never depart."

Why are these things in me?

Alexander had never asked that question of himself. He knew only that the desire to see what lay beyond the horizon had been in him since boyhood. Until this moment, the awareness of its presence had been enough for him. But the conversation with Rodriquez, showing him how different he was from the ordinary run of men, was arousing within him not only the question but the sharp desire to answer it.

Why this love of travel?

Perhaps one answer was to be found in the very era in which he had been born in Berlin on September 14, 1769. It was an era of restlessness, an age of searching westward. All Europe had been looking in that direction for the nearly three hundred years since Columbus had stumbled onto the New World; and there had been thousands in Europe not content merely to look; they had sailed out in the wake of the Genoese navigator. The French and English and Dutch and Germans had felled timber, held off Indian attacks, and hammered out farms, settlements, forts, and fisheries in Canada and North America. The Spanish, killing the Aztecs' Montezuma and crushing the Incas and Mayans, had established their garrisons throughout Mexico, Central and South America.

And the new horizons to which men of the era had looked had not only been physical. They had been political and philosophic as well. The age of freedom, heralded by smoking muskets and the blood-smeared guillotine, had taken its place in history. When Alexander was six years old, American Minutemen had fired on the troops of General "Blundering" Thomas Gage at Lexington. Within another two decades, the common people of France arose to crush the monarchy that had ruled them for centuries. Two months before Alexander's twentieth birthday, the Bastille was stormed and fell.

Yes, it was a restless age and Alexander was certain that, in some mysterious manner, a goodly bit of that restlessness had rubbed itself into his being at birth.

The second answer to his question was one of a more personal nature.

He was raised at the family estate, Tegel, just outside

Potsdam and a few hours drive from Berlin. The house at Tegel was huge and magnificent. Spacious lawns swept down from it to a pine forest where a small lake, circled by sandy beaches, could be found. On a nearby hill, the land had been cleared and grapevines and mulberry trees planted. On other hills were natural sandpits, excellent for the playing out of imaginative adventures. The estate should have been a paradise for the two Humboldt brothers, Alexander and Wilhelm.

But, for Alexander, it wasn't. It was, instead, a place of loneliness. His father, Major Alexander Georg von Humboldt, an officer in the army of Frederick the Great, had died when the boy was ten. His mother, Maria Elisabeth, was known to all her friends—and to her younger son—as a prim, reserved woman incapable of warmth and affection. An old acquaintance once described her as "Somewhat pale, with finely drawn features that on no occasion betrayed emotion." Maria Elisabeth viewed the education of her sons in history, the classics, and foreign languages by tutors as a duty. But she could not—or would not—see the necessity of displaying a mother's love.

This lack of affection seemed not to trouble Wilhelm at all. He was an alert, happy youngster, adept at lessons and games, and with ambitions for a literary career. But Alexander felt Maria Elisabeth's coolness keenly and, in the main, found lessons tedious. And so he turned to the warmth and vitality of literature, devouring, first, *Robinson Crusoe* and then the adventures of the globe-circling Captains Cook and Bougainville and of the New Zealand and Australian explorers, Vancouver and Flinders. There, in those books, he found men who really knew how to live; and in those books, he discovered the sort of life he wanted to lead. Someday he would sail out into the unknown as they had sailed and would explore as they had explored.

The desire for travel and adventure is all too often nothing more than a boyhood yearning that fades into a vague, bittersweet memory with the coming of manhood. But not so with Alexander; in him the urge to travel persisted through the years, following him to the University of Göttingen, where he became friends with Georg Forster, who had accompanied Captain Cook on his second voyage around the world. Georg Forster, explorer and writer: now there was a man. He had sailed into uncharted seas. He had stridden the beaches of tropic islands. He had climbed lava-covered mountains and had peered into the craters of steaming volcanoes. He had sat at the fires of strange, ebony-skinned peoples. Forster's vivid accounts of his experiences in distant, wild places had hammered Alexander's boyhood yearning into an adult obsession. It was an obsession that would haunt him for the rest of his days, just as it haunted him and tugged at the roots of his being this very night at the stern rail of the *Pizarro*.

There was a third and final answer to the question of his love for and need to travel. It was probably the truest of the lot. It was his work.

From earliest childhood, he had been drawn to the forest of Tegel. For a lonely boy, it was the perfect spot for dreaming of future adventures and pretending he was exploring strange lands. But the forest also called him for quite another reason and one equally wonderful. It abounded in all types of natural life. Birds nested in branches; ants bored their cities into the soft, dark earth; spiders spun delicate webs among the bushes; flowers spread themselves over the ground, and vines and moss crawled up the trunks of trees; reeds thrust their slender yellow-green shoots up from the water of the lake; and rocks, some lusterless and some glistening, lay in patches of sunlight.

But these things were not toys to the boy. Alexander did

not want to play with the butterflies and lizards and worms and spiders and frogs he captured, the flowers and rocks and weeds he collected. He wanted to study them. He wanted to learn their names. He wanted to know how the tiny creatures he found breathed and moved and searched out their food. Did they have hearts and blood and muscles? How did they see? How did they hear? He wanted to know how pine cones came to have their peculiar shapes, and how flowers nourished themselves and why they bloomed at certain times and then slept, brown and withered, at other times. What was beneath the hard surfaces of rocks? Why and how had they come to be in the forest? For how many years —how many centuries—had they been there?

There was an endless array of puzzles to be encountered there in the forest at Tegel—all the fascinating puzzles that the mind of an enthusiastic young natural scientist must encounter.

Through all his early years, Alexander's love of science developed side by side with his love of travel. At his insistence, the marvelous lightning rod of the American Quaker, Dr. Benjamin Franklin, was installed atop the main house at Tegel, making it the second building in Europe to be so protected. He sketched countless pictures of the plant and animal life in his beloved forest; the skill with brush and pen that he developed would serve him well in later days in another land. The most memorable acquaintances of his youth—botanist Karl Ludwig Willdenow, tutor Joachim Campe, and physician Marcus Herz—were those with whom he could discuss the workings of nature and the latest scientific wonders that were changing man's concept of the physical world: Count Alessandro Volta's experiments in electricity; James Watt's steam engine; Antoine-Laurent Lavoisier's recognition of the importance of oxygen in the transformation of chemical elements; and Immanuel Kant's theory of planetary origin.

He wanted to study for a career in the natural sciences when, after a boyhood of tutoring and several months spent at the University of Frankfort, he entered the University of Göttingen at the age of twenty. But his mother pressed her lips into a thin line and shook her head. Science? No indeed. It was all well and good to pass the time of childhood painting pretty pictures of flowers and collecting rocks and butterflies. But now her younger son was a man and must face the fact that science was a career for the dreamers and the impractical ones of the world. He, Alexander, must learn to be practical, like brother Wilhelm who was now preparing for a career in law. He must calm that restless heart of his and turn to a study of economy and finance. Ah, they were excellent subjects, quite befitting one of his noble birth. They could lead to positions of importance in banking, in the military, or in the government.

And so the aspiring explorer-scientist spent his days at Göttingen in classes in literature, philosophy, mathematics, history, and finance. But he could not keep away from science, particularly in a school so interested in that field. He found time for research in the various properties of plants. He went to Berlin to see the giant balloon which Blanchard had built and in which he had crossed the English Channel. He chatted with his fellow students, among them Ernest August, soon to be King of Hanover, and the future astronomer Jabbo Oltmanns, about Henry Cavendish's discovery of the chemical constitution of water, and about William Herschel's finding of the planet Uranus. He attended the classes of Johann Friedrich Blumenbach and listened, enrapt, to his lectures on his new system of comparative anatomy and the races of mankind. Then over to Christian Gottlob Heyne's classroom he went to hear that scientist's halting but brilliant discourses on the history of civilizations.

And his scientific interests sometimes carried him far from the University. During a vacation in 1789, the year the French Revolution erupted, he toured the upper reaches of the Rhine. The importance of that journey to his future career was to remain with him for the rest of his days. In the shadow of castles overhanging the river, he poked among rocks, dropping some into his geologist's sack and hammering others to dust, and wondered at their chemical content and why some were similar to and others different from those he had read about in distant regions. He squinted at the towering, purple mountains and puzzled over the fact that only certain types of plants and trees could be found at certain altitudes. And he recalled the questions he had asked himself in his classes in the history of civilizations—why were the peoples of one place on the globe, of one climate, of one altitude, so different from the peoples of another. There, in the clear air of the Upper Rhine, he sensed that there was a common solution to all these mysteries.

Then a curtain was raised somewhere in his mind, and light poured in. Alexander had touched upon his first scientific theory.

His face glowed with excitement in the light of the campfire that night as he put his theory into words for his traveling companion, Van Geuns. "There is a harmony in nature, an invisible harmony. All natural objects are interrelated. We cannot study rocks by themselves. They must be studied in their relationship to surrounding soils and plants. They are not cast down on the land by accident. They are what they are because of the land in which they are found. Find a certain type of soil and a certain type of plant and you will find a certain type of rock. And it is the same with plants. They are related to their soil, their climate, their altitude. What else can account for the fact that one kind of plant will flourish and another will die in exactly the same spot? And as for human beings: are we not related to—perhaps it is better to say influenced by—our natural surroundings? Doesn't that account for the very obvious fact that inhabitants of mountainous regions differ so very decidedly from dwellers on plains?"

The interrelation of all natural objects—minerals, rocks, soils, plants, animals, and even human beings: it was a revolutionary concept for his time. Not since Aristotle had man envisioned nature as of one grand design, with all its parts related to and dependent on each other. It was to be a cornerstone of Humboldt's whole scientific career.

Warming his hands over the campfire that night on the Rhine, Alexander looked beyond the theory itself and saw what it could do to his life. Suddenly, he saw travel in his life as not merely a desire but a necessity. Now he *had* to travel. Like all theories, his had to be tested and proved. One can not study the relationships in nature while sitting in the comfort of one's home. One has to get out into the world—into every corner of it that one can reach—if one is to test and prove a glorious theory.

Now, after exactly ten years of waiting and other work, the theory had finally brought Alexander von Humboldt to the deck of the *Pizarro* and his westward journey. As he had written to a friend just before sailing out of La Coruña, it demanded that, first and foremost among all his tasks in South America, Humboldt discover "how nature's forces act upon one another, and in what manner the geographic environment exerts its influence on plants and animals. *In short, I must find out about the harmony in nature.*"

There. He had his answers. The restlessness of the age,

his own venturesome spirit, and his scientific work—all these forces had melded in him to account for his compulsion to travel.

Alexander turned from the stern rail to face Captain Rodriquez. Perhaps he could put into words what he had just fathomed of himself. But he saw that Rodriquez was over at the wheel talking in low tones with his helmsman. It was too late to resume their conversation. Perhaps it was best that he did not have to speak with Rodriquez again. He was certain the Captain would not understand him. And he was not quite sure that he understood himself.

His eyes returned to the sea, now covered with a mist that had come up to the level of the rail. Somewhere, in the near distance, was the island of Tenerife and the city of Santa Cruz. They would dock there in the morning.

CHAPTER THREE

Laboratories of Pain

"Look at that!"

Aimé's cry, startled and jubilant, rang out a few minutes after the *Pizarro's* anchor had crashed down into the water of Santa Cruz harbor. During the pre-dawn hours, the ship had moved cautiously out of a rough sea and toward its anchorage, laboring through a yellow-white mist so thick that passengers and crew were unable to distinguish any object beyond a few cables' length. The town and the volcano of Teyde behind it were completely hidden from view.

Then, just as the anchor had been let go, a sharp wind blasting out from the shore had begun to shred the mist. The first rays of the sun had illumined the peak of Teyde and had spread their pale light down over the barren slopes of black rock to the flat-roofed crescent that was Santa Cruz. Alexander admired Captain Rodriquez's skill; he had cursed and coaxed his ship to an anchorage directly below the town's fort and its protecting guns.

Rodriquez himself had smiled grimly at his handiwork

and had gazed up at the muzzles of the cannon. "Those guns will attend to any British ship that might be so rash as to come into the harbor after us. They know how to handle the British. They took off Admiral Nelson's good right arm when he tried to capture Santa Cruz two years ago."

It was at that moment that Aimé shouted and pointed out beyond the harbor entrance.

Rodriquez turned quickly, then stared. Four English vessels stood in the dissolving mist, no more than a mile offshore.

"It's a miracle we got past them," Aimé breathed.

"No miracle, my friend," Alexander said. "Just the fog. The very same mist that made our entry into the harbor difficult saved us from them."

"But if the fog had blown away just twenty minutes earlier—"

"Then, at this moment," Rodriquez said, "we would have a nice English Lieutenant aboard telling us politely but firmly how much his Captain would enjoy our company on the trip back to Portugal." Rodriquez spat into the green harbor water. "I wish they would come in after us. It would be the pleasure of a lifetime to watch them blasted out of the sea. Spain has lost too many good men to those British."

The Captain gave the ships one last smouldering look and then, seeming to shrug them and the thoughts of old sea battles from his mind, turned to Alexander and Aimé.

"The orders I received at La Coruña instructed me to stop here long enough for you to climb Teyde."

"Yes. And also to study the rest of the island."

Rodriquez ran squinting eyes up the black, treeless face of the volcano. "How high is it, Baron?"

"It has several peaks," Alexander said. "The highest is over 12,000 feet. That's the one we will climb."

Rodriquez snorted. "And probably break your necks in the bargain. And for what? The view? The air? They're just as good at sea."

"For neither. But there are many other things we want to see, things that only a climb can show us. Tenerife's vegetation at various levels. How great our endurance will be for the coming hardships of the New World. What it is like to walk up the side of a volcano." Alexander smiled. "You see, we're very curious men."

"Well, then, you'd best get to your business on the island quickly," Rodriquez advised. He nodded briefly toward the British ships. "They have a good stretch of water to patrol and they will have to raise anchor soon, whether they like it or not. I want to be away before others come to take their places."

Alexander and Aimé hurried ashore. Immediately after being welcomed by a group of local officials, they went into the streets of Santa Cruz in search of guides for the Teyde climb. They found the air suffocating. The town was painted over with a wild assortment of colors: the ebony slopes of Teyde tumbled directly down to white houses with red roofs; the ground underfoot was a mingling of gray and brown and black hues; yet, somehow, out of that depressing surface surged papaw and banana trees, poincianas and roses, vines and ferns in a tangle of dazzling greens and yellows and pinks and whites. They came across a thirty foot Carrara marble statue of Our Lady of Candelaria, commemorating a miraculous appearance of the Virgin in 1392 near Guimar. They located a shabby Dominican library of just a few hundred aging volumes.

But the two Europeans found no guides. Not one of the residents of Santa Cruz had ever been inspired to venture up Teyde. And, Alexander concluded, they could not be blamed. The volcano had been there, bleak and intimidating, all their lives. It was a nuisance, belching out its lava and stinking gases from time to time, as it had just last year.

"Why climb it?" was their attitude. "It is difficult enough just to live in its shadow."

And so, the following morning, the explorers hiked over to the nearby port of Orotava and, without difficulty, located guides. On the western shore of Tenerife, no one was bored with or frightened of Teyde, for here the volcano showed a different facet of its personality to the islanders. The shoulders of ugly black rock were gone, replaced by laurel and pine forests and plateaus of sand shimmering in the heat. The slopes looked soft and inviting as they swept upward to a peak glinting pink in the sunlight.

At Orotava Alexander and Aimé also found three distinguished citizens as companions—Messieurs le Gros and Lalande, the latter the secretary to the French Consulate at Santa Cruz, and the angular Thomas Appleton, an English gardener living quite peaceably here among his country's enemies.

The climb was scheduled for the next day. Alexander spent a worried night anticipating it. He was not afraid of the dangers involved. Rather, he was a little frightened of himself. He looked on the climb as a test of his ability to withstand the coming physical hardships of South America. A man can be consumed by an ambition; yet something beyond his control can prevent him from realizing that ambition. With Alexander it could be his ill health. Throughout his boyhood, he had been frail and sickly, prone to coughs, headaches, dizzy spells, and frequent bouts of ague. Such ailments and others—a year-long struggle with fever, for one—had pursued him into his adulthood, and now he seriously questioned his ability to stand up to real bone-breaking and muscle-splitting hardship. If he lacked that ability, all his grand plans for the New World were doomed to failure. Tomorrow would tell the story.

Alexander watched himself closely—even trying to time his heartbeat—as he started off through the dawn with his companions. At first, there was nothing to worry about, for the ascent up out of Orotava was gradual, leading them along a narrow, stony path through a forest of chestnut trees to a grove of laurels where brambles, waist high, covered the ground. They rested in the shade of the only fir tree in sight. Below, the streets of Orotava looked as blue as the Atlantic beyond them, an optical effect caused by the fact that each thoroughfare had a gully of water coursing through it to wash away refuse. Off to Alexander's right, a clear spring bubbled up out of the earth.

The climb became more difficult as they moved up steep slopes and then dropped into narrow ravines that invariably led to even steeper slopes. Far above them, the summit of Teyde was lost in a yellow haze. Bracken tore at their legs. At their approach, birds scattered wildly into the air from nearby bushes. Lizards darted across their path. With a shock of fear, Alexander realized he was no longer breathing, but gasping, and that a little knifelike pain was stabbing outward from somewhere deep in his chest.

The pain intensified with his every step. It became a thin, ever-tightening wire band about his chest by the time the climbers had passed through an area of ferns with sharp green spindles that struck at their faces. In a forest of juniper and pines, wrecked by hurricanes, he became aware that his fingers and legs were numb. Waves of giddiness flowed over him and, whenever one of his companions spoke to him, he could only nod in reply.

Then, towards the middle of the day, when they were far up the volcano, the climbers moved past the rock of Gayta and entered the Llano del Retama, an area of nine square leagues covered with the fine dust of pumice stone. Alexander gasped when he saw it. Here, his strength would be tested once and for all. All the day, surrounded by rich vegetation, he had had to remind himself that he was scaling a volcano. Now such reminders were unnecessary. The temperature rose as the land turned arid and forbidding. No birds flew overhead; the only animals seen were a few rabbits and goats, dusty things that, appearing briefly, managed to look as sinister as the surrounding landscape. The climbers found themselves threading their way around obsidian blocks that had been hurled out of the crater several thousand feet above their heads. More often than not, they stumbled over the blocks, for a raw, hot wind swept directly into their faces, whipping up the pumice dust and flinging it into their eyes, driving it up their nostrils and into their mouths, where it clogged their throats and lay dry and gritty on their teeth.

For more than two hours, they were in this swirling, angry desert. After the first half hour, Alexander was certain he had come to the end of his journey. The fear of his questionable strength reached a throbbing crescendo, then dissolved into a self-pity alien to his nature. It wasn't fair that he should have been drenched by the quicksilver of wanderlust and then not be given a body to match his ambitions! There was so much to be done in South America, so many valuable studies to be made. He had the brains for such studies, but not the physical strength. . . .

He blundered into a chunk of obsidian and fell forward on his hands and knees. Tears of pain filled his eyes, turning the pumice dust on his lids to gray mud. He blinked, his head sunk between his shoulders, and his hands came swimming into focus. Covered with gray dust, they no longer looked like hands, but like the trembling claws of some dying beast.

The fear that had become self-pity now suddenly hardened into anger. The mountain had thrown him down on all fours, just as if he were an animal. Well, he was *not* an animal and he would not go on looking like one. Even if Teyde defeated him, he would not crawl or be dragged from it. He would walk off, proud and upright. But he would not be beaten. At least, not just yet. Too much was at stake.

It required all his strength to haul himself to his feet; and then strength he did not possess to shove one numb, trembling leg out in front of himself and then follow it with the other—until he was actually walking again. His heart was pounding against his ribs and the roar of blood in his ears drowned out the shriek of the wind. Now he moved bent far over, partly to keep the stinging pumice dust out of his eyes, but mostly to enable himself to breathe. His arms hung limply at his sides. He forced himself to swing them in an effort to bolster his spirits; what resulted was a look of monkeylike, pitiful jauntiness. His throat kept closing, causing him to gag, filling him with the fear that he would drop to his knees and vomit on the sand. He knew that if he fell again he would never be able to rise.

Then, shortly after he had become convinced that he would remain in this choking desert for all eternity, the ground underfoot slowly hardened. Walls of earth appeared on either side and Alexander found himself in a narrow ravine, free of the Llano del Retama and its fierce wind. By comparison, the air in the ravine seemed thin, silent, and crystal clear.

Halting, he wanted to sink to the ground and release his grip on all his muscles. But he held himself erect, watching his companions come to a stop about him. They were gasping and coughing and were coated from head to foot with pumice dust. Their faces were streaked where perspiration had caked the gray powder into thickish lines of mud. Let them decide what to do, he thought; let them decide whether to go on or rest. He would not betray his weakness by being the first to drop to the ground. The men gaped stupidly at each other for a long moment.

Then gardener Thomas Appleton said with true English economy, "Not exactly a stroll through the park, was it?"

And then they all sat down, quite suddenly.

They made camp several hours later in a small cavern in the rocks. Located above a plateau, it was called Estancia de los Ingleses.

"It means English Halt," Monsieur Lalande explained. "In earlier days, most of the visitors to Teyde were Englishmen. Mules could bring them up this far. The rest of the way had to be done on foot. Most of them preferred to go no further."

"Mules?" cried Aimé. "You mean we could have *ridden* this far?"

"Yes."

Bonpland regarded his dusty front sourly. "Well, this is certainly a fine time to tell us."

The men cooked dinner over a small fire built in the entrance to the cavern. Then, after watching the sun sink below the Atlantic, they settled themselves on smooth boulders for sleep. But, for Alexander, sleep was impossible. Warming himself by the fire as the mountain air fell to just above freezing, he remembered how at sunset he had glanced up to the summit of Teyde, that purple cone called El Piton, and had realized the hardest part of the climb still lay in the future. He had come through this day successfully—if but by the skin of his teeth. But what of tomorrow? How well would he stand up to it, worn raw as he was by today's exertions?

It was a question that, in his present state, it was best not to pursue. He leaned back against a boulder and closed his eyes, trying to tell himself that everything would be all right. After all, he *had* made it through this day. And, after all, there had been other times of hardship in his life.

His mind lingered on the second fact. Yes, he had faced hardships before, perhaps in not such a concentrated dose as today, but difficult and wearing just the same. Why hadn't he thought of them before? Why hadn't he used them down on the Llano del Retama to bolster his spirits? He realized it was because he had been all too human. He had been too much the prisoner of the day's discomforts and fears to recall them to mind. Then, with a start, he realized he had never considered them as hardships until this moment; he had always looked upon them as simply normal adjuncts to his work. Perhaps it had required an experience such as today's to see them in their true light. Indeed, they had been hardships, without a doubt, and there had been many of them throughout the years.

First, after he had been graduated from Göttingen and had spent several unhappy months at the Hamburg School of Commerce, he had decided to concentrate his scientific talents on the field of geology and had applied for work with the German Ministry of Industry and Mines. The reply ordered him to the training school at Freiburg; several months later, after intensive instruction in geology and mining, he was appointed Inspector of Mines in the gold-veined Beyreuth and Fichtel mountains.

The job had delighted him, freeing him as it did from the gloomy prospect of a career in finance.

Even his mother was pleased. "No matter if it is in science," Frau von Humboldt said, "it is, at least, a government position. Now, my son, you will see. It will lead to better things and all those foolish notions about travel will be forgotten."

What an exacting, responsible position it turned out to be

for a twenty-three-year old. It required that he survey mining sites and check the ore output at operations in such sprawling areas as Bohemia, Thuringia, and Mansfeld; it sent him underground daily on inspection tours of airless tunnels filled with the dank smell of the earth and of the sweating bodies of the men who worked down there. What he saw appalled and infuriated him.

"Those tunnels aren't fit for animals," he cried to fellow mine officials. "Many of them aren't properly shored up. Some are filled with poison gases. Has anyone here ever given a thought to safety devices for those men?"

"Of course," was the answer, usually followed by a rather vague wave of the hand. "But there are so many other things that we must attend to—"

He brushed such lame replies aside, thinking savagely that at least he did not have so much to do that he could not think of the welfare of the laborers in his district. Such thinking led him to establish at the village of Steben in 1793 Germany's first training school for mine labor. He followed it with others throughout the area, each stressing the latest in safety measures and instilling in the miners a fresh pride in their work.

That alone should have been enough to insure him lasting fame in the field of mining; it was positively revolutionary for a government official to show concern for the welfare of the miners. But Humboldt was not one to rest on his laurels. Still alarmed at the poisonous gases he found underground, he invented a respirator to protect the workers against them. That task almost cost him his life. Once, investigating a contaminated tunnel, he lost consciousness. Only the quickness of a foreman in dragging him outside saved him from death.

Even at the end of his regular workday, during those five years in the mines, he would not rest. He went instead in search of the chemical properties of the mosses and lichens he found growing on the walls of shafts and tunnels, asking himself, "Why do they possess the startling ability to grow in stifling darkness, away from fresh air and sunlight?" This after-hours study resulted in his first important scientific paper, *Frieberg Flora,* published in 1793.

No sooner had he finished the paper than he became interested in the experiments of Luigi Galvani, the Italian physiologist after whom galvanism, the flow of electricity as produced by chemical action, was named. For more than twenty years, that scientist had been investigating the effect of electricity upon the nerves and muscles of animals. In 1789, he had demonstrated that an electric current can be conducted from a frog's nerve to its muscles; using two different metals, he had placed one in contact with a nerve in the little animal and the other with a muscle, causing the latter to contract, suddenly and involuntarily.

Always so easily inspired, Alexander decided to carry Galvani's experiments a step further. "Galvani induced animal nerve and muscle actions with electricity. Why not try the same thing with *animal and human organs?*" he told shocked friends. "Who can tell what good it might do? Might it not reveal that 'mysterious life force' in all living things? Might it not prove of some value in the treatment of functional disorders in humans?"

From rocks and plants, he switched to collecting all sorts of tiny animals, particularly frogs. Dissecting them and placing them on his microscope stage, he subjected them to electric shocks. Fascinated, he saw hearts and blood vessels contract and a watery liquid begin to flow from the blood of wounds. He studied the effect of oxygen and carbon dioxide on heart pulsation.

Then he turned on himself to study the effects of galvanism on the functions of the human body. In these experiments, he bore up under severe pain and great danger in the hope of lighting the way to the treatment of certain types of human suffering, and his friends sagely observed, "He's not going to be happy until he kills himself."

And, for a while, it looked as if that was exactly what he was trying to do. Once, he subjected a cavity left in his jaw by a tooth extraction to electric shock in an effort to anesthetize it. The attempt was unsuccessful; the world would have to wait a while longer for painless surgery. The frightening details of another experiment were described in a 1795 letter to his former Göttingen professor, Johann Blumenbach:

"I applied two plasters to my back, each the size of a thaler, covering the trapezoid and deltoid muscles respectively. Meanwhile, I lay flat on my stomach. When blisters appeared, they were cut, and contact was made with zinc and silver. I then felt a violent, painful throbbing, so severe that the trapezoid muscle swelled considerably, the throbbing sensation being conducted to the base of my skull and the spinal processes of my vertebrae. . . . Frogs on my back hopped about, even when the nerve was not in immediate contact with the zinc, but separated from it half an inch . . . my wound serving as conductor. My right shoulder was until then principally affected. It pained considerably, and the lymphatic, serous liquid, produced with even greater frequency by the irritation, was red. As in the case of bad sores, it turned out to be so corrosive as to inflame my skin in red streams where it ran down my back. . . . After being washed, my back looked for many hours like that of a man having run the gauntlet."

The results of these harrowing ventures—there were some 4,000 of them, performed on both animals and himself—were made public at the end of five years, in 1797, in the form of two books. Those works would go down in scientific history as pointing the way to the development of electrotherapy.

Although the scientists of his day could not know this, they were well aware that he had wiped away much of the mist shrouding the functions of the human body. They proclaimed him a genius, a pioneer in physiological research.

And how did Alexander von Humboldt react to all the acclaim? He turned his back on it, just as he turned his back on his promotion to Counselor at the Upper Court of Mines. And for what? Why, to travel, of course.

His restlessness and his wanderlust were not diminished by his success in the mines and the laboratory. After that first important geologic excursion along the Rhine while at Göttingen, he traveled through France, Belgium, and England with his friend, the inspiring Georg Forster. Then, later, on vacations from the mines, he visited an old friend of the family, poet Johann Goethe, at Jena, tramped across the Bernese Alps, and talked with physicist Marc-Auguste Pictet at Geneva.

Back at the mines and laboratory, while deep in midnight-black tunnels or dissecting frogs, he dreamed constantly of future trips—real expeditions that would illumine for the eyes of Europe the natural wonders of strange lands. Perhaps he would go up to Russia and cross to Siberia. Perhaps to the New World. Perhaps to the South Seas.

"I've got to get away," he told himself again and again. "I don't like Germany. No matter if it's my homeland, I don't like it. The people are cold and dull. There's no imagination here. Everyone is in a very comfortable little rut all of his own. I have got to get away soon. And no one can stop me. Not my mother. Not Wilhelm. Not the Minister of Mines himself."

His chance to "get away" came in 1796, much sooner than he had anticipated—and different from the way he had wanted it. In November of that year, Frau von Humboldt died of cancer at Berlin. When his grief and shock had passed, Alexander looked up to find himself financially independent, the recipient of an inheritance of 95,000 thalers. No longer need he work to live. No longer need he frustrate his ambitions just to please his mother. He now had the financial means and the freedom to make his dreamed-of expeditions realities.

And so, investing his inheritance to assure himself an annual income of over 3,000 thalers, he had put the mines and his galvanic experiments behind him. He went to Paris and began the series of adventures that had finally brought him to this night far up the face of Teyde.

Sleepily, Alexander gazed at the dying fire. Surely, he had nothing to fear from Teyde and South America. He had lived through hardships before—laboratories of pain, he called them—and they had prepared him well for future trials. The mine tunnels had raised havoc with his lungs, plaguing him with colds and rheumatic pains, but he had gone back into those tunnels time and again and they had not killed him. A doctor had advised him to stop his galvanic experiments on himself, warning that, "You are destroying what little health you have and are driving yourself to a very early grave." He had ignored that pessimistic medico and here he was, not in a box under the ground, but almost 12,000 feet up a mountain. Now he must learn to ignore his own fears. There was no time for fear. There was too much to see and do.

Alexander finally slept.

The final assault on El Piton, the summit of Teyde, began at three o'clock in the morning, and the base of the summit was reached an hour after dawn. Alexander sat down to rest and to take pleased stock of himself. He was gasping in the thin air and his hands were torn by lava rocks. Cold perspiration coated his face and the wire band was cinched tight about his chest, but he paid no attention to them. He felt like a man born anew. It was as if the brief review of the years between Göttingen and Teyde had lifted a thousand-pound weight from his shoulders. The problem of health would never bother him again.

He heard Aimé's voice, ironic and amused, off to his right. "Well, what do we do now?"

He saw that Aimé was standing with his feet planted wide apart and with his hands on hips and with his head thrown far back, staring up the side of El Piton. Enclosing the crater of Teyde, it ascended almost vertically, looking as if God had played a joke on the mountain by topping it with a giant dunce's cap. The dunce's cap was grotesquely festooned with volcanic ash and chunks of lava.

"How will we get to the top?" Aimé went on. "There's not a single place for a foothold."

"But there is," Alexander said, after a moment. He pointed to a cluster of black rock twenty yards along the curving wall. Above it, twisting down from the top of the cone and looking like a humping, thick stream of congealed blood, was a long current of ancient lava. "We will find plenty of footholds there."

Aimé's hand swept over the men and up the steep wall. He arched his brows comically. "Gentlemen, thus far we have been mountain climbing. Now we shall be reduced to mountain crawling."

Crawling. What an apt word that proved to be! Alexander led the men to the base of the lava flow and that was the last time they stood erect for the next half hour. The first forty yards up the cone saw them doubled over like prehistoric creatures, their hands grabbing at rocks, their feet moving constantly in quest of solid support. All the while, the wall steepened and, with each step, Alexander felt his chest sinking closer to the earth until, at one point, he found himself sprawled flat against the jagged lava. Cautiously, his hand went above his head, searching for and then closing over a rock. He brought one knee up level with his stomach and started to pull himself upward. The rock crumbled in his grasp. The pieces bounded and skidded past his face. He slipped downward several feet, coming to rest alongside Aimé.

The two friends gaped, speechless, at each other, remembering that Captain Charles Baudin had almost met his death several years ago in a fall from this very spot. Alexander dug his knees into the cone as though it were an arch enemy and thrust himself up over and past the ground he had lost. Angrily, without pause, without looking back, he fought this lumpy, razor-sharp headdress of Teyde. Sometimes he was on all fours, sometimes on the balls of his feet and the tips of his fingers, sometimes flat on his stomach. Then, before he was fully aware of what had happened, the struggle was over. His outstretched fingers went spidering over flat ground; they were followed by his head and shoulders; then he was standing atop Teyde, 12,500 feet above the sea.

An icy wind blasted him and he fought to get his breath. Then he pulled Aimé up alongside him. They fell back against the low ridge of lava and pitchstone that separated them from the crater. In a few moments, they would go one hundred feet down into that crater; they would sniff at its gases and marvel at how sulphurous vapors had turned its walls snow-white; they would record its temperatures at various levels; and Humboldt would here begin the study that, after craters all across South America and Mexico had been visited, would tell the world of the relationship between volcanoes and the interior of the earth and would give that world its first maps of volcanoes.

But, for now, Alexander had strength enough only to lean

against the lava ridge and let his eyes roam over the world circling him. Overhead was the dark blue vault of heaven. Beyond and below the tips of his shoes were slopes of tumbled rocks and gray pumice dust, then forests of juniper and pines stretching down to other forests of chestnuts and laurels. Far below, there were great, long swaths of fern, groves of banana and coconut trees, red-roofed villages, wide beaches, and, finally, the Atlantic.

Aimé was making a strange noise deep in his throat. It was supposed to be a laugh. "Oh, how I envy you, my friend. If you only knew how much I wanted to quit this whole business last night. But you—you looked as though you had been born for this mountain."

Alexander could not bring himself to look at his friend. Born for this mountain. He shook his head. Oh, Aimé, if only *you* knew. Someday, someday far away from here, I will tell you the truth.

He looked westward over the Atlantic and saw the horizon, rigid and sharp against a cloudless sky. It seemed to be beckoning. . . .

CHAPTER FOUR

Venezuela

THE 16TH OF JULY, 1799, was a date to remember.

The *Pizarro* was forty-one days out of La Coruña. At six o'clock in the morning, Bonpland and Humboldt came on deck to see the coast of Venezuela, the country that, in their day, was a collection of seven united provinces known as the Captaincy General of Venezuela. The coast, humped with mountains, stood low and hazy and purple on the southern horizon.

Three hours later, with the sky an unwrinkled curtain of dazzling blue falling away on all sides from the sun, the *Pizarro* was in the Manzanares River and running up to her anchorage at the battery of Boca, a mile out from the city of Cumaná.

The jibs came crumpling down to the bowsprit; gallants were hauled in; seamen moved forward to await Rodriquez's shout to let go the anchor. Alexander and Aimé, their faces childishly eager, hurried from the port to the starboard rail and back again in search of the best possible view of the circling hills and the plain that ran back from the shore to Cumaná and its castle with walls looking a dusty gray in the distance.

Each man had held his own vision of how a tropic shore would look. This stretch of northern Venezuela, in the province of New Andalusia, not only lived up to their expectations but surpassed them. Everything stood out sharply and clearly in the morning air. Ships from Spain, native dugouts, and rafts crowded the anchorage; welcoming shouts came to them over the water. Cacao trees thrust their trunks up to heights of sixty feet above the sandy beaches, dwarfing the mimosas that mingled with them, and spread their branches like umbrellas. Clustered about the bases of the trees and spread out over the plain were cassia and caper shrubs. The distant hills gleamed whitely in the sunlight and were pocked with the green lumps of cacti. Egrets flew overhead. Flamingos, and alcatras—brown pelicans the size of swans—posed majestically in the shallows.

Aimé gripped the rail with excited hands. "All my life, I've waited for this moment. I didn't know when it would come or in what country. But I knew it would come." He laughed helplessly. "And, now that it is here, it deserves a fine word or two. But I can't think of a single thing to say."

Alexander nodded understandingly. "When I learned that we had changed our course and were going to miss Cuba, I was disappointed. But now I'm not."

Aimé glanced over his shoulder and his expression sobered. Coming up on deck were several passengers, who looked more like skeletons than human beings. They were deathly pale and the skin clung loosely to the bones in their faces. There were great dark stains under their eyes. Their appearance and Alexander's words recalled to Aimé's mind the last grim days of the Atlantic crossing.

Everything had gone well until then. They had devoted

their days to fishing, measuring the flow of ocean currents and the temperature of the water, and shooting the sun; during the nighttime the two explorer-scientists searched the heavens, sighing when they sighted the Southern Cross, proof that they were at last in tropical waters.

Then, suddenly, a shadow fell across the ship. Typhoid fever moved with terrifying efficiency through the hot, airless sleeping quarters below deck. Within three days, two sailors and more than a half-dozen passengers, among them the Negroes from Guinea, were ill. Aimé, forgetting that he was a botanist and remembering only his years as a naval surgeon, joined another physician on board in fighting the sickness. But it was a losing battle. By the end of the week, death claimed the *Pizarro's* youngest passenger, a Spanish youth bound for the New World with the fanciful hope of carrying a fortune back to his widowed mother.

At night, just a few hours after the boy's body had slipped quietly into the sea, Captain Rodriquez summoned Alexander and Aimé to the quarterdeck. His expression, as usual, was stormy, but his face was gray and drawn; though for the world he would not have openly admitted it to anyone, he had grown very fond of the boy in the days since La Coruña. When the ship's bell had tolled the dead man's knell that morning, Alexander had discerned tears in the seaman's narrow, unblinking eyes.

"I have news for you," Rodriquez said. "I'm changing course tonight. Away from Cuba. To the south."

It required a moment for the explorers to digest this information. Then Aimé asked quietly. "Because of the typhoid?"

Rodriquez had no need to reply directly. The answer was obvious. "I've got to get these people off this ship before they all die."

"We understand, Captain," Alexander said. "Where will we make port?"

"At Cumaná. On the northern coast of New Andalusia." Rodriquez studied the tips of his boots. "I'm sorry to do this to you. You will have to change all your plans. But it can not be helped."

"Of course. Perhaps we will see Cuba later on."

The remainder of the voyage, with the specter of death hanging over it, had been completed in gloomy silence. But now, with the cacao trees standing green against an azure sky and a heat haze shimmering over distant Cumaná, the explorers felt their spirits rise. They must put thoughts of death behind them. They must forget the disappointment of missing Cuba. They were in South America. That was all that mattered. And these shores could keep a geologist and a botanist busy for a lifetime.

There was a rattle of chain and the crash of water as the anchor was dropped. The *Pizarro* shivered as its forward progress was halted. Dugouts, filled with cheering natives, sped toward the vessel. The passengers lined the rails, shouting their relief to be so close to land again.

Alexander turned to see Rodriquez grinning at him from the quarterdeck. He was as pleased as his passengers to have his pestilence-laden ship safe in port.

"Well, it's done," he shouted with unusual gaiety. "You are across the Atlantic."

Alexander cupped his hands about his mouth to make himself heard above the noise. "Yes. But our work is just beginning!"

An hour later, they were ashore with their equipment.

The next three days passed in a haze for the explorers. They walked into Cumaná, finding it still largely in ruins from the earthquake that had leveled it recently, and were welcomed by the Governor of New Andalusia, Don Vicente Emparán. They rented a spacious house, and were wined and dined by the Spanish dignitaries of the city while they tried to get down to work.

Work?

The word was laughable when they thought of how the days passed. Alexander and Aimé were like children confronted with thousands of magnificent new toys. Daily, they picked up hundreds of objects—rocks, handfuls of sand, strangely wrought shells, and plants—only to discard each in a matter of seconds for something more striking, more exotic.

They idled away many hours in the houses of natives, eating unfamiliar seafoods from coconut shells in the shade of palmetto roofs, and sitting on chairs that were really blocks of coral cast up from the Atlantic.

They sailed a short distance along the Manzanares to watch the African slaves on a plantation dance about a campfire to the savage, monotonous strumming of a guitar.

And, as Alexander wrote in his notebook, they found a local mode of bathing curious: "We every evening visited a family, in the suburb of the Guayquerias. In a fine moonlight night, chairs were placed in the water; men and women were lightly clothed, as in some baths of the north of Europe; and the family and strangers, assembled in the river, passed some hours in smoking cigars and talking. . . ."

But soon they put the time of play behind them. They divided their time between the sea and the land; Alexander happily noted similarities between European and South American land and rock formations, further proof of his theory of the interrelation of all natural objects; he drew sixty sketches of Venezuelan plants, and other drawings to illustrate the comparative anatomy of shellfish; he determined the latitude of fifteen sites for a map of the interior that he was planning; he measured the height of the coastal ranges; and he and Aimé collected some 1,600 plants, among them 600 new species.

The natural wonders they encountered never failed to astonish them. Once, on a hill outside Cumaná, they came upon a forest of cactus and opuntia (prickly pear) thirty to forty feet high. They measured the trunk of one cactus and found it to be four feet nine inches in circumference. A native told them proudly, "Its wood becomes very hard with age. We use it for the doors of our houses."

August, September, and October passed quickly. Alexander studied the languages of the Chayma and Tamanac Indians, noting their similarities as he filled his notebook with such strange words as:

Chayma	*Tamanac*	
Ure	Ure	(I)
Tuna	Tuna	(Water)
Je	Jeje	(Tree)
Piache	Psiache	(Physician, Sorcerer)
Guane	Uane	(Honey)
Ata	Aute	(House)

In October, Humboldt lived through his first earthquake.

And at half past two in the morning of November 11, Aimé dashed into his room and shook him awake.

"Alex! Alex! Come outside quickly!"

The explorer tumbled out of bed. He groped for his robe. Aimé gave him not a moment to slip into it, but grabbed his arm and dragged him out onto the verandah, explaining excitedly, "I got up a few minutes ago to get a breath of fresh air. And I saw the most amazing thing. Look!"

The coolness of the air fully awakened Alexander. Aimé pointed skyward. Alexander's eyes followed the direction his friend indicated. He gasped, stepped forward quickly, grasped the ornate iron railing running along the porch.

Tumbling across the black heavens was a giant display of unearthly white fireworks.

Without lowering his eyes, Alexander caught Aimé's arm and pulled him to his side. "A meteor shower!"

"Shower?" Aimé cried. "It looks more like a storm, if you ask me!"

Hundreds of "shooting stars"—bolides—traced brilliant paths across the sky, flowing over the horizon from the east-northeast and flashing off toward the south, all of them leaving luminous trails from five to ten degrees long. Each meteor had a very distinct nucleus, appearing to Alexander as large as the disc of Jupiter; the bolides continually exploded, casting sparks off in all directions.

The two explorers watched in awe-struck silence for more than a minute. Then the sky darkened as the meteors disappeared over the southern horizon. "Have you ever seen anything like that in all your life?" Aimé asked.

Alexander raised an excited hand. "Wait. There will be more."

True to his words, in a few minutes the eastern horizon glowed as if the sun were directly behind it, and another swirling, flaming, exploding parade of white arced across the sky. The spectacle, broken by short spells of darkness, lasted for more than three hours, bringing thousands of meteors into view.

When Alexander finally left the verandah at dawn, he wrote an account of what he had witnessed to friends in Europe. What he had seen was one of the greatest showers of meteors of all time. It had swirled across Brazil and Venezuela to central Europe and had marked the beginning of astronomy's understanding of the periodicity of such showers. Humboldt's measurements and observations of the shower at Cumaná helped astronomers to the recognition of that periodicity and to a greater understanding of the nature of asteroids.

Since October, the explorers had felt a tide of restlessness rising within themselves. They had given several months of labor to New Andalusia. It was time to move on to new areas. But where? The entire continent, every inch of it inviting, dropped away for thousands of squarc miles to the east and south and west. Where should they go next?

"The Orinoco River?" Alexander asked. It was as much a suggestion as a question.

Aimé smiled knowingly. "To find where it connects with the Amazon system?"

"Yes. I can not think of a more worthy undertaking." Alexander removed a map from its leather case and spread it flat on a table. The river sprawled across the cream-colored page, flowing up from the southwest and emptying into the Atlantic roughly one hundred miles below Cumaná. Alexander's finger stabbed the Venezuelan coastline. "Up here, it flows into the Atlantic with such force that, when Columbus came upon it, his ships could not make headway against it, even with all their sails spread. It caused him to reason that he had come upon a great continent. A river with such a current couldn't rise out of a mere island. It needed a vast land mass to gather such force."

Now his finger moved along the curving black line that was the river. "But, down here, past the tributaries of the Apure and the Meta, all the maps become very confused. Each shows a different way in which the Orinoco is connected with the Amazon. But not one of them shows the correct way. Not one. Because not one of the map-makers or explorers ever bothered to find exactly how and where the rivers are joined."

"But there is no doubt that they *are* joined," Aimé put in, caught up in Alexander's enthusiasm. "All the people we have talked to here in Cumaná say they are connected. They say the Orinoco system joins the Río Negro and that the Río Negro then flows into the Amazon. They say the Indians and many of the missionaries have been using that connection for years."

"I know. And they're right. But what they say and what the maps show are two entirely different things. That is because the maps are based on those made years ago, when South America was first invaded by the Spanish. Here, wait a moment." Alexander produced a second map. "Look at this one. It's based on a map made by Sir Walter Raleigh when he went in search of the golden city of Manoa. Manoa! Golden city!" He snorted with derision. "A very convenient legend invented by some very wise Indians to rid themselves of the bothersome Spanish by sending them in search of the pot of gold at the end of the rainbow. But never mind the legend. Look at the map. See how it shows the Orinoco and Amazon running side by side. Down here, between them, is a giant lake. Both rivers flow into it. It's nonsense!"

He rolled up the maps and returned them to their case. "It is my belief that the maps of old were made by two types of people: tellers of tales who never traveled all the way up the Orinoco, but went only so far and then left the rest to their imaginations; and those who based their maps on Indian legends and descriptions."

"There is a third kind," Aimé said. "Those who simply did not know how to make a map or had no equipment with which to make an accurate one."

"Yes. And we're different from the whole lot of them. We're not believers in legend. We *will* make the entire trip. And we have the instruments for accurate map-making."

Alexander's voice raced like that of a Cumaná street peddler. "We have the chance to do this country a real service: find the exact spot where the Orinoco joins the Río Negro, thereby linking it with the Amazon. We can rip away years of legend and confusion. The knowledge of where those systems join can be of great importance to the future development of this country. It can facilitate trade and settlement. It can make friends of countless Indian tribes that are strangers to each other." His eyes were shining like a child's. "Aimé, it's the place for us. Oh, the things we can do! Collect plants . . . see the land, the people—" He broke off abruptly, breathless. "Well, what do you think?"

Aimé massaged his chin, shrugged, then smiled.

"I think I will enjoy a ride up the Orinoco very much."

They were on their way to the Orinoco by the end of November, first crossing over to Caracas to outline their plans to the Catholic bishop there and obtain from him a letter requesting the missionaries to the south to help them along their journey.

They remained at Caracas until February, 1800, collecting plants, surveying the coast ranges, climbing the Silla de Caracas, and visiting Lake Valencia. Then, after a short visit to the city of Puerto Cabello, they dropped south and entered the *llanos* of Venezuela, one hundred and fifty miles of plains falling away to the settlement of San Fernando, located on the Apure River, one of the principal tributaries of the Orinoco. It was their plan to sail down the Apure and into the Orinoco.

The journey across the llanos was one to remember for a lifetime.

They drank milk from the famous "cow tree" of the area. A native struck the tree with a knife, and a thick white liquid poured into a gourd. Aimé studied it suspiciously; it might be poisonous. But Alexander, without hesitation, lifted the gourd to his lips and his eyes widened with amazement. The fluid tasted exactly like milk! A bit acid to the tongue, it was, but as creamy as that brought from a cow.

Then, at Calaboza, they heard of eels that, upwards of a yard in length and living in nearby muddy streams, gave out shocks of electric current.

"Electric eels?" Aimé cried. "This is too much, really! I don't believe a word of it."

"But it is true, Señor," a native of the area assured him. "I have seen them kill horses and men."

"Then we must see them." That, of course, was Alexander, always curious, always a little too daring for his own good.

"No, no!" the native objected. "No one is safe near them. Just be content to hear of them and then be on your way."

But Alexander would be neither "content" nor "on his way" until he saw these fabulous, frightening creatures. Hadn't he studied animal electricity in the Bayreuth and Fichtel mountains? How could he now depart without seeing animals that actually possessed their own electrical plants? And, naturally, he had to see them when they were alive.

"Alive?" the native echoed, aghast. "But that is impossible! Not one of my people would dare go near them."

Alexander extended his hand and opened it. In his palm lay a small pyramid of coins. "They are for the men who will bring me a live electric eel."

The coins turned the trick. A dozen natives volunteered for the eel hunt. It began with the driving of a herd of horses into a nearby stream. The hunters, armed with slender harpoons, strung themselves out along either bank and climbed into trees overhanging the water. At first, the horses, in need of a cooling drink, took to the water happily, unaware that they had been assigned the evil task of stamping the eels up from the muddy bottom. Within minutes, a long, tubular, brown body flashed on the surface, followed by another, and then another. Sudden panic gripped the horses as the disturbed eels swam against them and released their savage currents of electricity. Standing on the bank, Alexander and Aimé gasped. The horses, restrained from escaping the river by a group of natives stationed along either shore, crashed blindly into each other, their manes swirling about their necks. Some went down on their knees with the force of the shocks and were mauled by flaying hoofs as they tried to rise again. Others, losing consciousness, slid to their deaths below the surface. Again and again, the flashing tubular bodies were glimpsed through the churning water. Harpoons shot out from the shore and down from the trees. They glinted briefly in the sunlight.

It was over in five minutes. The line of natives along the water's edge dissolved and what was left of the terrified herd of horses bolted out of the river and dashed over the sun-baked earth. One after the other, harpoons were flung down on the sand. Their points were embedded in wiggling bodies that twisted themselves into a writhing mass of brown near Alexander's feet.

"Careful! Careful, Señor!" the natives shouted as Alexander moved to the catch.

"I'll be all right–"

The sentence ended in a strangled cry. He had accidentally stepped on one of the twisting creatures. A shock of pain knifed up his leg and, hot and numbing, spread out through his entire body. The breath was torn out of him and he went down on his knees in the sand, instinctively flinging himself away from the eels. He came back up quickly, but he limped for hours to come. He later recalled in a letter home: "I do not remember of ever having received from the discharge of a large Leyden jar a more dreadful shock than that which I experienced. I was affected during the rest of the day with a violent pain in the knee and in almost every joint."

This personal lesson in the might of the eels did not prevent him from measuring and dissecting them in the next days and then returning to the river to study further their living habits. He noted that they are usually three to five feet in length and that their bodies are scaleless; he located the bundled network of fibers, later termed the "bundles of Sachs" and the "organs of Hunter," which give them their electric power; he found that they live quietly along the river floor until disturbed by some intruder, at which time they rouse each other with violent shocks and rise in a body to attack that unfortunate. He gave these tubular creatures with their large and ugly heads the name *Electrophorus electricus.*

Thus was discovered for science one of the strangest and most terrifying beings in that always strange and sometimes frightening realm, the animal world.

The llanos of Venezuela fell slowly away behind the explorers, gradually replaced by the rolling hills and shallow valleys and forests through which the Apure River cut a mile wide, yellow-brown swath. At last they came to the tiny settlement of San Fernando on the banks of the Apure, eighty miles from its juncture with the Orinoco. Here the travelers rested while a boat was provisioned for their river journey. Their stay lasted for three days—until four o'clock in the afternoon of March 30, 1800.

At that moment, Alexander came out on the verandah of the mud and reed hut adjoining the local Capuchin mission and faced his host of the past days, Father José Maria de Malaga. He extended his hand.

"All is ready for us, Padre. There remains nothing to do but thank you for your hospitality. You have made our time here at San Fernando pass most pleasantly."

The Capuchin monk shook his head. Alexander could not help but smile. Father José struck him as a brown-faced replica of that friar—what was his name?—in the English legends of Robin Hood. He was balding and he was pudgy and soft looking. Yet he must be as strong as that other priest—Friar Tuck, that was the name—for he had lived in perfect health in this fever-ridden country for close on a decade. "No, no, Baron," Father José was saying. "It is I who must thank you. You broke completely the monotony of life here in our little town. Always my people will remember you and Señor Bonpland, measuring the width of our Apure and showing us your little machine that told us our air is full of electricity. No, we shall not forget you soon. And we shall pray that someday you will pass this way again."

"Perhaps we shall, Padre. I most certainly hope so."

Turning, Alexander stepped from the verandah and into the blinding sunlight. The air was moist and thick. Great swollen clouds stood motionless on the horizon. A hot wind was blowing in from the south. All were signs that the rainy season was arriving on schedule. It was due to begin in April. It would last until September. It wouldn't do a thing, Alexander thought wryly, to facilitate their journey.

A dirt path, flanked by stones, fell like a bent arrow from Father José's dwelling to an unpainted, rotting wharf. At the moment, the path was crowded, the entire population of San Fernando having turned out to bid their visitors farewell. There were Achaguas, Guajibo, and Tamanac Indians, all of them flat-faced, broad of nose, and heavy of eyelid, their bodies of rippling muscle naked to the waist. And there were the Spanish settlers, as black and as naked as the Indians, with only their narrow faces and pointed beards proclaiming them to be of a different race. The crowd broke in front of Alexander and Father José and then closed in behind them to follow them down to the dock. Alexander found himself smiling and nodding in every direction and feeling very much like a departing monarch.

The last of the people stepped aside and he had an unobstructed view of the boat—a *lancha,* the Indians called it—in which he and Aimé would spend the next weeks of their lives. As before, he was struck by the fragile look of the thing. No more than an exceedingly long and slender canoe, it seemed little or no match for the rapids and whirlpools that Father José warned lay ahead. Two-and-a-half feet wide, it had a warped mast amidships. Near the stern, the Indians had built an open cabin, a *toldo,* the floor of which extended far out over each gunwale. Under its roof of palm leaves had been placed a staggering array of supplies—eggs, plantains, cacao beans, cassava cakes, tobacco for trading with the peoples along the Orinoco, firearms, fishing tackle, and, of course, the scientific gear that had become as much a part of Alexander and Aimé as their arms and legs. The weight of the toldo and these many necessities pushed the stern so far down that the bow of the canoe was clear of the water. Aimé, checking the provisions for the final time, was in the toldo and when he saw Alexander he hurried amidships and jumped to the dock. The lancha rocked so violently that the outer edges of the cabin floor slapped the water. Alexander winced, then smiled philosophically. Perhaps the rapids and whirlpools would mean nothing to the boat after the bull-like Aimé.

The Frenchman came grinning up the path. "Alex, you should see the gift Father José put aboard for us early this afternoon." He swung his smile to the monk. "Our thanks,

Padre. Only a man long in this climate would have thought of it."

"A gift?" Alexander asked. "What sort of gift, Padre?"

"It was nothing, really," the Capuchin monk said, nevertheless looking very pleased. "A bit of sherry wine—all the way from Madrid—and a basket of oranges and tamarinds. To make cooling beverages. You will soon find that this country is at its hottest during the rainy season. They may help to keep the head clear at times."

"That was very thoughtful of you, Padre."

"And now, Baron, you must allow me to perform one last little service for you."

"But you have done so much already."

"This will take but a few seconds. I should like to bless your lancha. It is good to have God with you on the Orinoco."

"Of course, Padre."

"I was going to ask you to do that very thing—but I should have known you would think of it yourself," Aimé said.

Until then, the three men had conversed against a background of noise from the crowd. Now, as Father José placed his left hand against his chest and raised his right arm, the people of San Fernando, Indians and Spanish alike, fell silent. Several went down on their knees. Off to the right, a brown-skinned child sucked his thumb and stared at the priest out of wide eyes. Slowly, and with a simple, touching dignity, the fat little Capuchin made the sign of the cross. His Latin words moved through the hot, moist air and lost themselves in the roar of the Apure. The silence remained after he had finished speaking. His eyes —wise with the knowledge of this land and its endless terrors—seemed to assess the travelers for a long moment. Then he smiled suddenly. "You will have good fortune on the

Orinoco. You will do all the things that you have told me you plan to do. In my heart of hearts, I know this. God go with you."

It was as if the lightness of his words and his smile gave the people of San Fernando their voices again. Excited chattering broke out as Alexander and Aimé boarded the lancha. Four Indians sprang easily into the forward section of the boat and took up paddles. The pilot, whose name was Francisco, took his place at the stern. He was half Indian and half Spanish; and his strutting and constant show of bravado in the past days had not pleased the explorers at all. The townspeople, waving and shouting, stationed themselves along the bank. Eager hands ripped mooring ropes from the sagging wharf and threw them aboard. The lancha swung out into the soup-thick yellow water.

Aimé waved back at the crowd with an enthusiasm surpassing theirs. His shirt was clinging damply to his back. As he grinned over his shoulder at Alexander, he looked extremely handsome with his tousled black hair above a face that the sun had stained mahagony and the days in South America had carved lean.

"It's a wonderful start," he shouted.

"I hope it ends as well."

The wind, coming against them at an angle, made the setting of the sail impossible. Indian paddles dug deep into the yellow water. The canoe faced east fifty yards from shore. San Fernando began to slide past the stern. Over the heads of the townspeople, Alexander saw the palm roof of the mission and its thin, weatherbeaten cross slip toward the horizon. One rickety shack after another fell away until only the forest came down to the river. Back on the wharf, Father José now looked like a little boy dressed in some sort of long, odd gown.

In the distance, thunder crashed. But it was barely audible above the continuing and rhythmic shouts of "Vaya con Dios. Vaya. Vaya con Dios." Even after the town was out of sight the shouts could still be heard, echoing along the wide, yellow corridor that was the river.

CHAPTER FIVE

The Time of the Caribe and the Jaguar

IN THE FIVE DAYS that they were on the Apure they came to know the river as a staggering, bewildering thing. Sometimes it seemed insane, twisting its way past boulders and whirlpools; and perhaps it *was* insane, for what else did the low, vicious waves dissolving against the shore resemble but the greenish foam of madness? Sometimes it was straight and phlegmatic; sometimes so shallow that the lancha would go aground on a hidden sandbar or, with a sickening jolt, drive itself into a submerged tree stump. And sometimes, when seen through the first rains of the wet season, it looked dead, a dull brown-green, pocked with a thousand tiny, splashing pimples. Then, in the moist sunlight that followed, it came alive and glistened the color of scorched butter.

Along its edges ran narrow, muddy beaches. Behind them

were, first, the reddish *sauso* hedge—so level it looked as if it had been cut by man—and then the forests of cedar, mahogany, mimosa, and braziletto. Here and there, a spindly palm tree bent against the wind. Where the land was low, the limits of the river could not be determined, for it swelled with the rain and overran its banks and, as deep as fourteen feet, spread out for miles, driving people, venomous snakes, spiders, cows, and chickens to humps of earth that were often no more than an arm's length above the water and that were always in the shadow of the patient, wheeling zamuro vultures.

There were endless things to see during those five days; jaguars, crocodiles, tapirs, and monkeys coming through ragged holes in the sauso hedge to drink at the river; a flight of birds rising with heart-stopping suddenness above the trees momentarily to obliterate the sun and fill the air with the deafening beat of their wings; a group of sleeping crocodiles, oblivious of snow-white herons strutting along their backs and perching unconcernedly on their long snouts; flamingos covering every inch of space on a small island at mid-river.

There were so many things to see that the travelers found themselves dividing them into "times" to keep their experiences from blending into a confused mass of impressions. There was the time of the fire, when they watched a vast field of cane sugar blazing, accidentally set afire by wandering Indians. There was the time when hundreds of swallows had skimmed over the river minutes ahead of a heavy rainfall. And the time when they had seen the giant jaguar asleep on the beach, his forepaws resting delicately on the tapir he had just killed and on whom he would lazily feast when he awoke. And who could forget the time when they had slept in the house of the half-naked, whimsical, pompous Don Ignacio? The house hadn't been a house at all;

it had been a grove of trees. While torrents of rain had filled their hammocks, Don Ignacio had strutted up and down, congratulating them on their good fortune in finding the company of a respectable Spanish gentleman in this wilderness.

On the third day out, they came upon the time of the *caribe.*

It began with a shout from the pilot, a shout in which urgency and amusement were mingled. It brought Alexander and Aimé out of the toldo. Francisco was crouched over the tiller, his eyes on the distant shore. His body was tense. There was an expression of savage delight in his eyes.

"You are going to see some fine trouble very soon. Look!"

Over on the sandy beach, a group of some twenty crocodiles were sunning themselves, a most commonplace sight. As usual, they lay motionless, ignoring each other. Their green scales, coated with mud, glinted like bronze in the sun. Alexander guessed they were from sixteen to twenty-three feet long.

Then he saw what had captured the pilot's attention. Thirty yards upstream, a large herd of thick-nosed tapirs, called *chiquires* by the Indians, had come bustling onto the beach. They were about as large as pigs, but considerably more active. They sniffed their way over the sand and into the water.

"Now watch! The trouble comes!" Francisco exclaimed gleefully. His face glistened with perspiration. His broken teeth were yellow against purplish lips. Up forward, the Indians were resting on their paddles and watching the shore.

Alexander saw the current carry the first of the swimming chiquires down in front of the crocodiles. Suddenly, there was movement among the reptiles. A sixteen-foot back lifted itself, a tail swished with a graceful ease that was

The Orinoco Expedition
CARIBBEAN
SEA
TO CUBA
FROM SPAIN - 1799
PUERTO CABELLO
CARACAS
VALENCIA
CUMANÁ
BARCELONA
ATLANTIC
OCEAN
Maypure
SAN FERNANDO
Apure
Orinoco
ANGOSTURA
(CUIDAD BOLIVAR)
Cinaruco
Meta
VENEZUELA
Guaviare
Inirida
Atabapo
Orinoco
ESMERALDA
YAVITA
Pimichin
Guainia
Negro
Cassiquiare
Orinoco
SAN CARLOS
Negro
Negro Joins
with Amazon

sinister, and one giant started for the water. Alexander imagined he could hear the clinking of the beast's scales even at this distance. Like some terrible, bloated lizard seen in a nightmare, moving in a series of thrusting starts, the crocodile slipped into the water.

He was almost upon them before the chiquires saw him. The water churned violently with their frantic movements. Comical little faces and thick shoulders started to break away in all directions. Into their midst charged the crocodile. Giant jaws flew open, flicking water high, and snapped down again, closing over something brown and terrified. The movement of the water became so violent that the viewers could not see what was happening. But they knew without seeing. Death was there, grunting and bleeding in the water.

Francisco had come to his feet, forgetting the tiller completely. The lancha rocked violently as he hopped up and down carelessly, gleefully beating the air with his fists. "He's got him! He's got him!"

Alexander and Aimé exchanged disgusted glances. The creature at the tiller was not a human being. He had forgotten the Spanish blood in him; he had forgotten the Indian blood in him. A lifetime in this untamed land had pounded whatever soul had once been his to dust. He was more of an animal than the creatures in the water.

He dropped to his knees and thrust his face close to Alexander's. Grinning crazily, he stabbed the explorer's chest with his forefinger. "Suppose you were the little chiquires and you were caught in the crocodile's mouth. What would you do? It's something you should think about. It's something we all have to think about."

Other crocodiles were now sliding into the river, their jaws closing on brown writhing flesh. The water was boiling. The tapirs were swimming in all directions, spinning slowly in the swift current, their button eyes popping wide. Grunts of pain, the sounds of teeth shattering bone and of giant tails crashing down on the water reached the boat. A red stain engulfed all the animals.

Francisco rushed on. "I'll tell you what I would do in the chiquires' place. I'd do just what the little Uritico girl did. Ah, she was a sly one." His words were coming so fast that they could hardly be followed; his eyes were on the animals and they were wide and fascinated. "A crocodile got his teeth into her leg and started to drag her under. But she tricked him, that one. She turned and poked her fingers in his eyes." He threw back his head, laughing deliriously. "Now, there's a real woman for you! Much too dangerous for a man to marry. Much too dangerous for a crocodile to eat. Right in the eyes she poked him. He is very sensitive there. He opened his mouth and, before he knew it, she was safe on shore. Her leg was almost torn away, but she was safe–"

"Caribe! Caribe!"

The shouts, full of terror, came from the paddlers up forward. The words were strange to Alexander's and Aimé's ears and they swung their eyes shoreward. As the pilot had talked, a calmness had started to come again to the water. Crocodiles, with dead chiquires clamped between their teeth, were swinging indolently back to shore. The little tapirs who had avoided death were swimming at a safe distance, already seeming forgetful of the tragedy that had touched their number. The water was smoothing out, the panel of blood looking greasy and black on the yellow-green surface. Then, a split second before the paddlers screamed, that oily surface prickled in a thousand places, as if a bucket of pebbles had been emptied into it. The chiquires began to whirl in an agonizing dance.

"What is it?" Alexander demanded of the pilot. "What's happening?"

Francisco had fallen back against the tiller. His smile was ecstatic. This was the best of all, the climax of the entire struggle. "It is the *caribe* fish. A horrible little thing." He held his thumb and forefinger about five inches apart. "Only so big. He swims at the bottom of the river. But let just one drop of blood fall on the river and he comes to the surface—by the thousands—and he attacks anything in sight."

He pointed to the Indian paddlers. "Look at them! See how afraid they are! More of them than not have felt his little teeth."

Alexander came to his feet. Once again in this strange land he had come upon something of which he had never heard, something new and exciting, something he had to see for himself. He moved forward to the paddlers, pausing just long enough in the toldo to take up a fishing net he had used earlier that day. The Indians watched his approach with a mixture of dread and hate in their eyes. They had been around him long enough to know what he had in mind.

"Take us in to shore," he demanded.

For a moment, the Indians sat rigid and sullen. Only their eyes moved, flicking back and forth between the flashing water and the man above them with his hair flowing in the wind. Then one paddler leaned forward and pulled up a ragged trouser leg and Alexander found himself staring at a brown kneecap scarred with a crescent of tiny, jagged dots.

"Caribe," the Indian said.

Alexander shook his head. "You won't be hurt. I promise you. Now take me in to shore." When the men did not move, he shouted over his shoulder to the pilot, "Swing us shoreward!"

"No, Señor! Do not be a fool!"

Alexander stared. Francisco was no longer a grinning savage. He was cringing against the tiller, his face gray beneath its brown stain. A very brave fellow, Alexander thought contemptuously—brave at a distance. "Aimé, take the tiller!"

Aimé waved, then pushed the pilot aside, pleasuring in the roughness of the action. He pulled the tiller bar in against his stomach. The lancha swung broadside to the current. Muttering, the Indians took up their paddles. No course of action was left to them but to drive the boat through the school of caribes as swiftly as possible.

Alexander, holding the net in one hand, leaned far out over the gunwale as the slender craft came close to shore and entered the churning water.

Chiquires, bleeding from hundreds of tiny bites, swept by under the paddles. A drumming sound began as the caribes blindly charged against the shell of the lancha. Then Alexander saw them, thousands of tiny fish, some no longer than a man's forefinger, flashing against the surface of the river, diving, rising, whirling in tight circles, crashing into each other, snapping greedily at anything that blundered into their path.

The lancha was now broadside to the shore, faced in the direction of San Fernando. Alexander lowered the net into the water, right up to its handle. He felt the handle begin to dance and struggle against his grip. He brought the net up swiftly, held it just long enough to glimpse the molten silver it contained, and then dropped it to the bottom of the boat. The giant Indian paddlers scrambled away from it. They cringed together up at the bow, muttering, pulling their bare feet up against their thighs, gesturing meaninglessly.

After a few moments, Alexander spoke quietly to them.

"All right. Back to your paddles. They are all dead." His voice held no reproach.

The lancha swung eastward again. Aimé came to Alexander's side. The Indians averted their eyes with the shame frightened men feel after the moment of danger has passed. The fish were now a harmless-looking lot as Alexander removed them from the net. They were ash colored with a tinge of green to them; their bellies, gill covers, and ventral fins were a fine orange hue. Alexander ran an exploratory finger along the belly of one and found there a long cutting edge—the world's tiniest saw. He pried open the mouth, piercing his finger on teeth no larger than the points of needles.

"Looks innocent enough, doesn't he?" Aimé said.

Innocent? Yes, when dead. But, when alive, he was truly a little cannibal. Alexander looked back over his shoulder. The water was still churning and red-black with blood. Crocodiles were coming ashore, carrying the fleshy shreds that remained of their prey. Upstream and down, chiquires were limping across the sands, trailing thick streams of blood. Another battle was done in the war that had been declared the day the world was born and that would rage until the very second it disintegrated.

The excitement of the time of the caribe was soon lost in the excitement of all the other times, particularly those of work. Aimé collected plants, herbs, tree leaves, and fruit and classified them in the rocking boat or by campfires at night while vampire bats swarmed about his great head. Alexander, sextant and pen never out of reach, charted the course of the river and began the map that would be complete only when all of the Orinoco—or, as he spelled it, *Oronooko*—was behind him. Daily, he took readings of the earth's magnetic intensity and ventured into the forests to scribble endless notes on the geologic formations, minerals, and plant and animal life he encountered.

One such excursion led to the time of the jaguar. At noon of the fourth day out from San Fernando, when the lancha was up on the beach and dinner was cooking, he walked far along the shore to study at close hand a group of sleeping crocodiles. At one point, he stopped to pick up some spangles of mica agglomerated in the sand and found himself looking at the footprints of a jaguar.

He straightened. Very slowly. His eyes moved along the foliage to his right. He did not have to look very far. Eighty paces distant, lying in the shade of a ceiba tree, was a giant jaguar. Later, he told Aimé, "No tiger ever looked so large to me."

But at the moment he was in no mood to laugh. He felt his heart pound and the blood go out of his face. His first impulse was to turn and run. He quelled it instantly and forced himself to remember the advice the Indians had given him for just such a moment as this. Move slowly. Move naturally. Do nothing to upset the animal.

Fortunately, the jaguar's attention was fixed on a herd of capybaras crossing the river downstream. As Alexander later recalled, "I then began to return to camp, making a large circuit toward the edge of the water. As the distance increased, I thought I might accelerate my pace. How often was I tempted to look back in order to assure myself that I was not pursued! Happily I yielded tardily to this desire. The jaguar had remained motionless. These enormous cats with spotted robes are so well fed in countries abounding with capybaras, peccaries, and deer, that they rarely attack men. I arrived at the boat out of breath and related my story to the Indians."

The encounter proved not to be Alexander's last with the jaguars on the Apure. On the last night of the voyage, just as the Indians were preparing to sling their hammocks on the Vuelto del Palmito, they discovered two of the great cats hiding behind a locust tree. A dash was made for the lancha and the night was finally passed on the hard ground of the island of Apurito.

The next day the river narrowed and grew shallow. The flow of water became sluggish. The lancha went aground on shoals on several occasions. The Indians paddled the boat close in to shore, then climbed overside and pulled it forward by means of a long rope lashed to the bow. Slowly the shore at their side fell behind them and Alexander found himself gazing out over a vast plain of water. It stretched away on all sides like an inland sea. Conflicting winds and currents gave birth to white-capped waves that crashed in over the gunwales. Several miles distant, mountains, thick with forests and huge boulders, thrust their peaks against a leaden, sullen sky.

Alexander had entered the Orinoco River.

Back at their paddles, the Indians swung the pitching lancha southward. Alexander squinted into the wind, eager to see all that the river had to show him. Dead ahead from him lay miles of hardship. Dead ahead lay uncounted readings of the earth's magnetic intensity, readings that in another decade would contribute to the establishment of a new scientific law. And dead ahead—far, far upstream—this awesome river, ever narrowing, finally joined with the Amazon system. If all went well, Humboldt would one day soon draw that point of connection on his map and cause all the other maps in the world to be changed.

CHAPTER SIX

Journey on the Orinoco

ALEXANDER COULD NOT help himself; he had to laugh. The first moments on the Orinoco should have been awe inspiring. Thanks to an all-too-human Aimé Bonpland, they turned out to be amusing.

A hard wind swept in from the east-northeast. Two Indians hoisted sail and the lancha plunged crazily into the swift current. Waves curled high on all sides, flinging the boat about as if it were a straw.

Spray lashed Alexander where he sat amidships with his back against Aimé's knees. Squinting, oblivious of the fact that he was wet through to the skin from head to foot, he scanned the distant shores—and distant they were, for the river, two miles wide at low water, had been swollen by the rains to a breadth of six miles. The giant rock called Punta Curiquina appeared dimly off to his left.

"I remember reading about that spot. In Father Gumilla's book of his travels," he shouted to Aimé without fully turning his head. "The Jesuits founded a mission there years ago. But they had to abandon it. At floodtide, the river surrounded it completely."

"How interesting," Aimé said at his shoulder.

The flatness of his friend's tone, its sound of disinterest—so alien to Aimé's customary manner of speech—caused Alexander to turn swiftly. What he saw first startled him. Then he started to grin.

Aimé's face was gray, with patches of green directly above his cheeks. He clutched the gunwales desperately. His shoulders were hunched, his eyes tightly shut.

"You're seasick!" Alexander announced.

Aimé opened his eyes and stared glassily at him. "Isn't that quite obvious?"

Alexander's grin erupted into an astonished laugh. "Not *you?*"

"Yes, me! And stop laughing!"

"I'm sorry. I can't help it."

"And I can't help being sick!"

"But this never happened on the Atlantic."

Aimé ventured a cautious turn of his head and glowered at the river. "This is worse than the Atlantic." He followed this observation with an agonized groan. He clamped his teeth together as the lancha slid, bucked, and rocked down the face of a wave. "See what I mean?"

"I do," Alexander admitted. "But try to forget it. There's so much to see."

Aimé smiled nastily. "I shall see it all, sooner or later—probably later." His words began to race. "But, right now, I think I'm going to be busy." He fell helplessly, urgently, across the gunwale.

Alexander shook his head sympathetically. After Aimé had been "busy" for a little while, Alexander settled his friend in the toldo and then returned his eyes to the somber forested mountains circling on the horizon. Far away to his right were the hills of Coruato, the retreat for wandering Indians expelled from the missions or their tribes.

The shouts of the Indian paddlers brought him to his feet and out of the cabin.

"Guaya! Guaya!"

"Caramana!"

One of the Indians had removed his paddle from the water and was waving it out over the bow. Alexander stooped low to peer beneath the spread of the sail. The lancha was aimed at the eastern shore and dead ahead lay a giant rock. It thrust its way up out of the Orinoco to a height of fifty feet.

Alexander swung aft to Francisco at the tiller. The pilot's black hair was plastered wetly against his forehead. His broken teeth were gritted against the river spray. A flight of spoonbills wheeled in low overhead.

Alexander crouched at his side. "What is it? What place is that?" He struggled to keep out of his voice the combination of pity and contempt he had felt for this man since the morning of the crocodiles and caribe fish.

Francisco seemed unaware—or uncaring—of the explorer's low regard for him. "It is the rock of Encaramada. The Indians call it Guaya and Caramana. There is a village at its base. We will land there—if this sin of a boat doesn't go under first."

The hulking mass of rock came into view above the sail. Alexander made out sagging huts set in its face and along its flattish summit. It was easy to see how the site had earned its name. *Encaramada* in Spanish meant "things raised upon each other." The rock was composed of rising tiers of granite slabs that gave it the appearance of a gargantuan, thoughtlessly constructed stairway. The familiarity of the scene struck Alexander so forcibly that, for a moment, he had the odd sensation that he had been here before, perhaps in some previous life. Then he realized that, with the exception of the huts, the rock formation resembled exactly many he had seen while working in the mines of Germany.

He moved to the gunwale. Now he could see the adobe and straw settlement curving along its base. His brows arched. With the sole exception of the fantastic Don Ignacio, he had not encountered a single human being all the way down the Apure. Now it looked as if that situation was about to be changed. Some fifty canoes and dugouts were lashed to the village wharf and he could make out great activity in the streets behind it.

The lancha docked and Alexander and Aimé, the latter still a bit unsteady on his feet, stepped ashore to find themselves in a busy and crowded village indeed. The air was filled with the babble of many tongues and the thick odor of wet wood burning and the stench of food cooking in unwashed kettles. Natives and Capuchin monks worked the barren soil about Mission San Luis del Encaramada. Ottomac, Tamanac, and Guajibo Indians wandered aimlessly along the waterfront or lounged about the campfires they had built throughout the town.

"They're stopping on their way south to the turtle egg hunt," Francisco said.

"Turtle egg hunt?" Alexander asked quickly. This was something new to him. "What's that?"

The pilot grinned slyly. It was good to know a few little facts that this very superior fellow from across the sea did not know. "It is an annual affair, Señor. All the Indians of the Orinoco depend on it for their living. Such a sight it is to see! Thousands and thousands of eggs are dug up and turned into a wonderful oil."

"Where does it take place?"

"To the south, Señor. To the south."

"Will we be able to see it?"

Ah, but it was a pleasure to see this proud Baron hanging on one's every word. It made up for all the cold looks of the past days. "Yes, Señor, you shall see it. I myself personally will take you to it."

"That's very kind of you," Alexander said brusquely, galled by the man's posturing. "Now I think you'd best attend to bringing fresh water aboard."

He turned swiftly from Francisco and continued his walk through town. Mingled among the Indians, he saw, were Spanish settlers who had fled their lowland homes in the face of the rising river; their women chattered and cooked; their children squabbled and squalled and ran happily underfoot. Seated in front of tents were glib traders from Angostura, their lips pressed thin and their eyes watchful as they guarded the casks of wine and bundles of tobacco heaped about them. Alexander learned that the wine and tobacco would soon be exchanged for the oil—and very good oil it was, the traders claimed—produced at the turtle egg hunt.

He and Aimé returned to the wharf in time to see two canoes of fearsome looking Carib Indians, en route to the turtle grounds, sweep up to the dock. Out came Alexander's notebook and, while Aimé peered over his shoulder and provided such helpful observations as, "I'll wager the word 'bath' isn't in their language," and "I've seen better specimens in a nightmare," he scribbled in his almost illegible hand:

"All are armed with bows and arrows. . . . All are smeared over with a plant dye, a brilliant red. . . . The chief, the furniture, the domestics, the boats—even the sails of palm leaves—are painted with this red. . . . The men are tall. . . . Their eyebrows are stained black. . . . Their faces are gloomy and hard. . . . The women are disgusting from their want of cleanliness. . . . They carry their children on their backs. . . . The little ones have their legs bound at certain distances by broad strips of cotton cloth. . . . This shapes the leg after the fashion of the country. . . ."

The writing of such descriptions was to become a highly important part of Alexander's work on the Orinoco. In future years, his word portraits would excite the imagination of all Europe and tear away the veil of mystery and ignorance surrounding the native peoples of South America.

Aimé slapped his friend's shoulder. "You use so many words, Alex. Why not simply write 'frightening and filthy'?"

The remainder of the morning was given to storing water aboard the lancha and sketching the juncture of the Apure and Orinoco into Alexander's ever growing map. Then the travelers were on their way again. Keeping close in to shore, they sailed past the mouth of the Río Cabullare. The next day, June 6th, saw them running along the base of the mountains of Encaramada and coming up to the rock of Tepu-mereme.

Tepu-mereme: the "painted rock." What fascination it held for Alexander! Here was not the history of South America today or even of the South America the day before Columbus arrived; here was the history of South America at the very dawn of time. High up on the gray face of the rock was a series of gigantic, crude drawings, fashioned by savages untold centuries ago. With Aimé, Alexander went ashore and threw his head far back to stare up at the grotesque figures.

"I can make out the sun and stars. And aren't they jaguars—those drawings over there?"

"Yes." Aimé pointed to the left. "And there are some crocodiles." The Frenchman lowered his head and massaged the back of his neck. His shrug was one of bewilderment. "How do you suppose the savages of an ancient day managed to gain that height with their brushes and pigments? The face of the rock is sheer. Even a modern engineer would have trouble building a scaffold to that height."

Aimé's question was answered a half-mile upstream at the camp of an old Tamanac Indian and his family. "It is very simple. Only a white man would not know. At the time of the great waters, our forefathers went to that height in their boats."

"The age of the waters?" Alexander asked.

The Tamanac was seated on his haunches in the sand. He smiled at these strangers with all the superiority of his many years. How ignorant they were. They came in splendid boats from across the sea. They wore fine clothes. They probably even knew the King of Spain. But they were very ignorant. He inclined his long, old face. "Does not the white man know of the great flood that came upon the earth in the earliest days of time, when the sea beat upon the rocks of Encaramada and all the men and women and children in the world perished?"

Alexander nodded. "I have heard of such a flood."

The ancient Indian's eyes glinted with amusement. Good. At least this grown stranger knows what the smallest Tamanac boy knows. Now we will see if he is even a little wiser than a child. "Then the white man must know how the human race was born again."

"I have heard of an ark—a great boat."

The Tamanac was too polite to laugh. He glanced warningly at his family. No one must laugh. The strangers must be educated. He said with great patience, "That is the story the fathers at the mission tell. But it is wrong. Very wrong. Have you not heard that a man and a woman saved themselves on a high mountain, called Tamanacu, on the banks of the Asiveru?" He spread his arms wide. His voice took on a chanting quality. "The man and the woman stood on the mountaintop with the great, angry waters swirling below them. They took in their hands the fruits of the mauritia palm tree and threw them behind themselves, over their heads, and, when they looked back, they saw the seeds in those fruits produce men and women who repeopled the earth." The Tamanac's hands fell to the ground. He stared inquiringly at Alexander, cocking his head a little to one side. "You do not know that story?"

"I know it—now," Alexander said quietly.

"And you will not forget it?"

"No. I won't forget it."

The Tamanac stood up. He smiled. "Good. All men should know the truth."

In the canoe, out on the river again, Aimé fell back against a gunwale. Laughter rolled out of him. "That poor old man. Looking down his nose at you because you didn't know his precious legend. You, who could show him knowledge that would make his head whirl. He's a child."

And on the shore, the aged Tamanac watched the lancha disappear around a bend in the river. He turned to his family. "How can a man reach his age without learning the truly important things in this world? It is too bad. He has the body of a man, but the mind of a boy."

Alexander sat quietly in the lancha. He was thinking that there is not only a harmony in nature, but a harmony in all mankind as well. Distances, varying languages and customs, and even the color of the skin had made a vast, complex, and often chaotic symphony of man's history. But everywhere in the complicated movements of that symphony were to be found the simple melodies of ancient traditions and beliefs. No matter in what land or in what era the symphony was played, those melodies were the same. He had heard one just now. He knew of Noah; the Indian knew of the mauritia seed; but they both knew of the great and terrifying deluge. To hear that melody of common knowledge in this savage land, thousands of miles from home, was to stand in the soft, gray air of the dawn of time and to understand afresh the concept of the family of man.

The lancha approached the island at eleven o'clock in the morning of April 7. The island was low and finger-shaped and set just slightly to the right of mid-river. From a distance, it was impossible to see that its shore was sandy, for close on two hundred beached canoes and dugouts hid it from view. They seemed like thick, gaudily painted splinters—curving sticks of red, purple, black, and green gleaming dully in the moist sunlight. Behind the boats were other colors and they were moving. Coming closer, Alexander saw these were the bodies of Indians crawling on their hands and knees in the sand or carrying small baskets toward several columns of smoke rising from the center of the island.

At the tiller, Francisco chortled. "I promised you a look at the turtle egg hunt. Well, this morning I am going to keep my promise."

The lancha slid rapidly toward the shore. The shadows of the warped masts of the beached dugouts reached out over the water to the bow. Added now to the activity on the beach was the sound of voices. Shouting children and their mothers ran to greet the new arrivals. A number of men abandoned their crawling to follow at a more dignified gait.

The children plunged into the river. They surrounded the lancha, their brown bodies creating a rising cloud of spray. Their faces were beaded with shining crystals of water. Their eyes were wide at the sight of the two white men above them. Their black hair whipped frenziedly about their shoulders. Fat hands with painted nails grabbed at the boat from all sides. Quivering in a cataract of soprano yelling and laughing, the lancha was pulled up on shore.

Alexander and Aimé stepped onto the sand and immediately found themselves at the center of a circle of painted faces and bodies. The men regarded them silently while the women pointed at their European clothing and giggled. The children tugged at their hands and showered water over them.

Francisco leaned far out over the bow. "You shall see many Indians this day, Señor. Enough to fill your little notebook. Caribs. Ottomacs. Tamanacs. Maypures. Guamos. They're all here—and don't they have a grand stink?"

Suddenly, a man in a tattered, stained black robe broke through the painted circle. In his own way, he was as frightening as the Indians. He was extremely tall and thin, but there was a look of hardness to him; across Alexander's mind flashed the picture of the masts of a ship without canvas. The hood of his robe was thrown back and the face above it was deeply lined and stained mahogany by the sun. His nose was a triangular hatchet, bony, with a shiny, hair-flecked knob immediately below the bridge. He was bald, but a tangle of black beard fell almost to his chest. He ran unblinking eyes over the explorers.

"I am Father Gomez of the mission at Urbana. May I inquire after your names and the nature of your business here among my people? Are you traders from Angostura?"

Alexander introduced himself and Aimé. "No, Padre, our business on the Orinoco is not trade."

Father Gomez came a step closer. "Not to trade? Then you're government officials. No? Soldiers? No?" Now he was glaring. "Priests?"

"No."

"I didn't think so. Then, in the name of all that is good and just, what is the nature of your business? Only trade or the priesthood or the government brings a white man to this miserable place."

"We're explorers, Padre. We're searching out the connection between the Orinoco and Amazon systems. We're mapping the river and meeting the people and taking readings of the earth's magnetic intensity."

Several seconds were required for Father Gomez to digest this information. Then he said, "I don't believe you."

"Why?"

"Why?" The priest's voice exploded from somewhere deep inside him. "How is it possible to believe that you have left your country to come and be devoured by mosquitos on this river for the pleasure of measuring lands that aren't your own?"

"Nevertheless, it is true," Alexander said. He took from a leather case his passport and the letter written by the bishop at Caracas. He handed them to the priest. "Perhaps this will convince you."

Father Gomez, his lips moving with the words, read the documents twice before returning them to Alexander. "You *do* tell me the truth." He shook his head and fingered his beard and grunted, "You must be quite mad."

Aimé grinned. "We are, Padre. You may take our word for it—we are."

A thunderclap of laughter erupted behind the black cloud of beard. "So are the rest of us on this river! Now let me make you welcome. Undoubtedly, you desire to watch my people collect the eggs?"

"Yes."

"And you shall. After we eat."

The explorers followed the priest to his tent at the center of the island; to one side of it were pits with fires burning in them, long wooden troughs filled with water, and piles of small jars and woven baskets; to the other side, a lean-to of palm leaves sheltered a makeshift altar.

While they ate a simple meal of fish and plantains, Father Gomez spoke knowingly on the business of searching out the turtle eggs. It was, he said, a highly important native industry. Traders from Angostura purchased the oil produced from the eggs for the lamps of the great Spanish cities to the north; the oil was also used by the Indians for their body paints and food; and, too, it found its way to the church lamps of the missions. The hunting season—called *cosecha,* the "harvest of the eggs"—lasted from March through April. The eggs were to be found on the Orinoco only south of its juncture with the Apure and were those of the *arrau* and *terekey* turtles. Father Gomez came yearly to the island during cosecha—"To celebrate the Mass daily and to govern the hunt. I must see to it that the natives do not destroy too many eggs through carelessness and that each tribe receives its fair share of ground."

Picking at his teeth with a fishbone, the missionary led the explorers down to the beach, explaining, "You came too late to see the start of the hunt. It began several days ago. I appointed a *commissionado del Padre* and he spent an entire day walking over the beach and thrusting a bamboo pole into the sand to find the soft spots where the eggs are buried. He measured out the area of the burial grounds and then assigned each tribe to a certain plot of ground."

They were now in the midst of perspiring, silent natives. They stopped near a man and a woman. The man was kneeling; the woman, his wife, stood patiently, placidly, above him. She smiled shyly at the visitors. Her face and shoulders were covered with an intricate design of criss-crossed black lines and red dots. She carried a sleeping infant on her back. The man was digging into the sand, his hands working like the paws of a dog, casting the sand off to his side. As he dug, his body went closer to the ground until, having reached a depth of approximately three feet, he was stretched out flat.

"He is almost to the eggs. They are usually no more than three feet down," Father Gomez said. To the Indian, he snapped, "Careful! Careful!"

The Indian straightened suddenly. He spoke briefly to his wife, shouted to two boys in the near distance, and flashed a smile at Father Gomez. In his hand was a small turtle, its legs moving wildly, its head sliding swiftly in and out of its shell.

"Hah! One of the eggs got away from you, did it?" Father Gomez laughed. "Hatched before you could get to it!"

The two boys called by the Indian came to him. He tossed the turtle to the taller of the two. They shouted with delight, turned swiftly, and ran off down the beach, throwing the tiny animal back and forth between them.

"They will play ball with it all day long," Father Gomez said.

The Indian thrust the upper part of his body into the hole. Out and onto the sand came grayish colored eggs. The woman placed them in a small basket and, when it was full, she joined a long parade of women flowing to and from the wooden troughs near Father Gomez' tent.

Alexander followed her. She shouldered her way up to one trough, broke the eggs, scattering the shells carelessly about her bare feet, and dropped the yolks into the water in the trough. Then she returned to her husband. Alexander managed to take her place at the trough. Other women of the tribe broke eggs and still others stirred the water with wooden spades. As he watched, a whitish oil spread over the surface. Working quickly and chattering all the while of tribal affairs, the women ladled the oil into kettles and placed it over the burning pits to boil. The finished product was then poured into earthen jars that were placed among hundreds clustered nearby.

Father Gomez joined Alexander. "The finished product is called tortoise butter." There was the sound of pride in his voice. "It can be compared to the best of olive oil. But when it goes bad—ugh!"

He led the explorer to the field of jars. "The three harvest grounds along this section of the river furnish five thousand of these jars of oil each year. Five thousand eggs are required to produce one single jar. Can you imagine how many eggs the arrau and terekey turtles lay?"

Alexander removed his notebook from his breast pocket. After a moment of multiplication, he stared unbelievingly at the priest. "But it seems an impossible figure! Twenty-five million eggs!"

"But it is a true one."

The men smiled briefly at each other. Their short friendship had come the full cycle. It was now Alexander's turn to doubt the priest's word. Father Gomez gestured happily at the notebook.

"Now," he instructed, "estimate that at least one third of the eggs laid are destroyed or are hatched out during the harvest. What, then, is the total?"

Again Alexander worked at the notebook. He shook his head. "Some thirty-three million eggs are laid annually."

Father Gomez nodded proudly. "A remarkable land, isn't it?" He kicked at the sand, suddenly thoughtful. "Maddening, but remarkable!"

The face and melody of the Orinoco changed constantly as the days carried the travelers southward.

Beyond the mouth of the Río Auraca, it was four nautical miles wide, a rising, thunderous thing in these first weeks of the rainy season. The air was moist and sticky and alive with mosquitos.

Then, at the strait of Baraquan, the river narrowed. Giant slabs of granite, devoid of vegetation, overhung the water. All seemed quiet. The throaty cries of jaguars, the screech of monkeys, and the chatter of birds were not heard. But, when the explorers listened carefully, they could detect the continual hum of the millions of insects living out their lives up on the rocks.

The river widened again. The land flattened. Past the mouths of the Suapure, the Caripo, and the Sinaruco rivers the lancha shot. At the beach of Pararuma, Francisco and the paddlers abandoned the expedition. Unfamiliar with the country ahead, they turned back for San Fernando. From Father Zea, the local priest, Alexander purchased a new canoe. He hired a pilot and paddlers and set them to building a toldo at the stern of the boat.

While the toldo was being constructed, Alexander and Aimé ventured into the surrounding forests. They brought back to the beach countless rock and plant specimens that would one day find their way to the museums of France and Germany. Aimé classified his plants and studied the pigments used for Indian body paints. Alexander continued his daily observations of the earth's magnetic intensity and brought his notes up to date. He told of the strange eating habits of the Otomaco Indians at the Mission of Uruana. During the rainy season, when it was impossible for them to fish, they avoided starvation by eating *poya,* small balls of earth.

"In their huts," he wrote, "we found heaps of these balls arranged in pyramids three to four feet high, each ball measuring two to four inches in diameter. . . . This earth is a very fine sticky substance of yellow grayish color, which turns red in roasting. . . . The Otomacos admitted that besides a few lizards, some fern roots, or a dead fish, they eat nothing for two months but this dead earth, of which they consume from three quarters of a pound to a pound in twenty-four hours."

The new canoe was ready for sailing in a day's time. Going down to the shore early in the morning, they found it to be a frightening thing. It was a tree trunk forty feet long, hollowed out by hatchet and fire, and so narrow that it could not accommodate three persons side by side. Cargo was piled high all along its length. A ragged sail flapped amidships. The toldo at the stern, set on a latticework of bamboo poles, was a rounded hut of palm leaves so low that a man could barely sit up in it. Whenever one of the paddlers moved, the boat rocked violently, seeming ready and more than willing to capsize at any moment.

"We're going into the land of the cataracts in *that?*" Aimé asked, aghast.

"I'm afraid so."

The giant Frenchman massaged his jaw. "I think I shall make out my will and send it back to France—right now!"

The two men stepped gingerly into the canoe. Listing badly, it swept out from shore and, turning south, rocketed through the churning water at the mouth of the Río Meta. Alexander and Aimé came to loathe the canoe. Neither could stand up without ordering the paddlers to lean far out over the sides to balance the thing. The toldo was suffocating; it protected only the upper parts of their bodies from the hot rain; their legs were exposed to the elements and were stretched far out over the water. They had to beach the craft every time they decided they needed to remove an item of scientific equipment from their supplies.

Their hatred extended from the canoe to the surrounding land. Not only were there thunderous rapids to plague them, but mosquitos, gnats, and flies swarmed out of the dripping forests and off the rocky faces of mountains to envelop them in hissing, black clouds; the Indians clamped their eyes shut and bent low and tense over their paddles, howling an incoherent chant. At night, huge red ants crawled up the legs of the men and chiggers traced stinging red welts across their stomachs. Worst of all were the *piumes,* so tiny that Alexander said they could fly through the eye of a needle. But they had the sting of wasps and each bite drew forth a spot of blood.

The days were now filled with the thunder of crashing water. Past the rapids at Ature, Javariveni, Canucari, and Garcita they struggled, sometimes driving the canoe straight into the wild, lashing water, more often heading into shore and carrying canoe and supplies through mud and over jagged rocks to the next smooth stretch of water.

At the beginning of the third week in April they came to the cataract called the Raudal de los Gauhibos, formed by a thick finger of boulder stretching across the river. Green water boiled white as it surged over low ridges and breaks in the rock and turned green again as it plunged toward the approaching canoe. A curtain of mist hovered above the entire width of the river, making a shimmering rainbow in the late afternoon sun.

Near the edge of the churning water, the new pilot ordered the Indians to rest on their paddles. He was a string-thin, cautious Tamanac in his late forties, a pleasant change from his predecessor. Aimé and Alexander, crouching near his feet, watched his eyes swing from the east to the west bank and then to them. He grinned a toothless grin.

"I don't know why I look at the shore. I have seen it a hundred times before and I know it is too steep and rocky for the men to carry the canoe over it. There is only one way for us. Straight ahead. Through the rapids." He pointed ahead. "You see that break in the rocks near the left bank? That is where we are going."

He shouted a single-word order. Paddles were thrust overside. The canoe shot ahead and rammed into the swirling, flashing water. In less than a minute, it was performing a frenzied dance. Time and again, it drove its bow beneath white curling walls of water, lifting its stern so high and with such force that the men seated there had to cling desperately to the gunwales to keep from being flung overboard. Then up would come the bow, twisting and spitting spray in all directions like some prehistoric river creature, and down hard—hard enough to loosen a man's teeth—would come the stern, the tiller almost ripping itself from the pilot's hands as it bit into the water. A palm leaf broke from the toldo roof. It whipped past Alexander's face and disappeared into the canoe's snarling wake.

Inch by inch, the log boat fought its way toward the break in the rock. When some twenty feet from it, the pilot half rose, still clutching the tiller, and shouted an order forward. Somehow he made his voice heard above the crash and hiss of the cataract.

Alexander and Aimé saw a giant Indian paddler respond to the order by getting to his feet. He dropped his paddle to the bottom of the boat. He stared for a moment at the water. The explorers saw the muscles in his back ripple as he pulled in a deep breath. Then he dove overside.

The canoe tilted crazily. Water rushed aboard, slopped aft to the cabin. Aimé cried in alarm for the man and started up. The pilot caught the Frenchman's sleeve. "Don't worry," he shouted. Water spilled over the edges of his brows and rolled down his cheeks. "He knows what he is doing!"

On their knees, stretching out over the gunwales as far as they dared, the explorers watched the Indian. He broke surface, facing them. He turned against the current. Foaming water covered him. Alexander groaned. The Indian reappeared, rolled over on his stomach, and began to swim toward the rock. His arms flashed brown and hard against the white water.

He crashed into the rock. His hands, fingers spread wide, shot upward, spidered over the face of the rock, and found a crevice. Slowly he lifted his dripping, shining body from the water. He clawed his way to the top of the boulder and dropped flat on his face. Alexander could see his back heaving convulsively. He remained prostrate for just a few seconds before coming to his feet to stand like a primeval god silhouetted against the rainbow mist with his big, thick-lipped mouth curling in a grin of pride and his arms outstretched to receive the rope that went snaking out from the bow of the canoe.

While the paddlers, chanting wildly and incoherently, put all their strength into each of their strokes, the Indian, his feet planted wide apart, hauled the rope in hand over hand. The canoe, bucking and surrendering palm leaves from the roof of the toldo to the boiling water, fishtailed up to the rock. Over the side went the paddlers, their bodies glinting briefly in the sun as they jumped onto little ledges now visible in the rising granite. They swung about with the natural grace of all savages and caught the starboard gunwale and pulled the length of the canoe flat against the boulder.

Alexander heard the pilot shouting close to his ear. "Out! Out! Quickly!" A hand struck his shoulder. Spray lashed his face. The yelling at his ear went on, sharp and clear and commanding above the deafening thunder of the river. "Go up to the top! We'll pass the supplies up to you."

Alexander came to his feet and, without hesitation, selected a ledge and jumped. His stomach, chest, and knees struck wet granite. For a second he felt he was going to topple backwards. He was dimly aware of Indians grabbing at him. He clawed at the rock, found a grip, and steadied himself.

He crawled to the level summit of the rock with Aimé, snorting like an exhausted buffalo, right behind him. Together, they noted their surroundings with wonder. Water crashed over the summit to their right and tumbled through a narrow break immediately to their left. But here, on the highest part of the boulder, they stood on a relatively dry surface, dampened only by the mist. Below them, the pilot and an Indian were tearing the lashings from the mounds of supplies while the other paddlers were forming a human chain up the side of the rock. Up that human chain, swung from one pair of brown hands to another, came the supplies to the explorers.

For close to twenty minutes, the two men worked in silence, receiving each bundle and adding it to the rising pile behind them. Now and again they groaned, as when Alexander found his carefully packaged notes sodden and pulpy. The water on their clothes turned to steam in the sunlight. Alexander glanced at Aimé. The Frenchman was a sight to frighten any civilized being. His trousers clung damply to his legs. One shirt sleeve was torn from wrist to elbow. His black hair fell wetly over the back of his collar and drained like a waterfall. His face was swollen, pimpled with the blood spots left by the piumes. His lips, always thick, were puffed to twice their normal size and were colored purple; his eyes were hidden behind narrow slits in two humps of reddish flesh. His hands were raw and bleeding.

Then Alexander looked at his own hands. The skin was gone from the knuckles. His fingernails were ridged with black, except for one ridged with blood. He laughed, realizing that he himself must look as savage and as filthy as Aimé.

When all the supplies were safe atop the rock, the pilot came up to the explorers and told them without condescension, "Now you rest for a while. There is nothing more for you to do. We know what must be done next. And we know how to do it. You will only be in the way."

And so, grateful without mentioning it, the explorers sat down for an hour and watched the Indians pull and then lift the canoe through the break in the rock. Twice it slipped backward and was saved from spinning off downstream only by the rope tied to its bow. When it was safe on the upper side of the break, the supplies were loaded into it and the travelers again took their places in the stern. By the time the sun had set, the Raudal de los Gauhibos was a mile behind them.

Two days later, they reached the mouth of the Atabapo River, a small tributary of the Orinoco. The Indians swung the canoe into this river of black water. They chanted quietly and failed to notice the triumphant glance that Alexander and Aimé exchanged.

The final stage of their journey was at hand. Their muddy clothes, the stinging bites of piumes, the steaming air, the suffocating clouds of mosquitos, the vicious rain—none of these things now mattered. Soon, very soon now, the question of three centuries would be answered.

Where—exactly where—do the Orinoco and Amazon systems connect?

CHAPTER SEVEN

The End of the Orinoco

ALEXANDER AND AIMÉ sat huddled together beneath what was left of the roof of the toldo. Rain pelted them with angry monotony and splashed over the skin-covered floor. Against Alexander's upthrust knees was set a soiled parchment map, a copy of one made a quarter of a century earlier by a Franciscan monk. He regarded it with a frown and said: "I don't know if it can be trusted, but for the time being we must put our faith in it." His finger traced the path of the southern Orinoco. "Here, just before reaching the Atabapo, the Orinoco, after running generally southwest, suddenly makes a sharp turn to the east. It continues past the Atabapo and the Casiquiare until it reaches its birthplace in the Parima mountains.

"It is the Casiquiare that interests us. See how it drops southwest from the Orinoco—at least, according to this map—to join with the Río Negro which, in turn, cuts down into Brazil to join with the Amazon. It is the Casiquiare which accomplishes the connection between the Orinoco and Amazon systems."

Aimé nodded patiently. He had seen the map and had heard Alexander's explanation a hundred times before. "And it still seems to me that, instead of turning into the Atabapo, we should have gone along the Orinoco to the Casiquiare and then turned there for the ride down to the Negro."

"That, I admit, would be the simplest way," Alexander said. "But the route we have chosen—"

"That *you* have chosen."

"All right. The route *I* have chosen. It will enable us to see more of the country. Look." A blackened fingernail moved along the twisting Atabapo. "See how it travels down to the Temi, and how the Temi flows on to the Tuamini—"

"And how the Tuamini brings us to the mission at Yavito," Aimé singsonged.

Alexander acknowledged his friend's misplaced sense of humor with a fleeting grin. "Yes. And see how a narrow stretch of land separates the mission from the little stream of Pimichin. And see how the Pimichin pours into the Río Negro after a short run to the southwest."

The explorer paused long enough to wipe away water gathering in his eyebrows. "We shall stop at Yavito, go overland to the Pimichin, down the Pimichin to the Negro, and along the Negro to the Casiquiare." His voice mounted with pleasure. "Then north along the Casiquiare back to the Orinoco. We shall have traveled in a rough circle—taking astronomical observations all the while—and we shall have shown where and exactly how the Orinoco and Amazon systems are joined."

Aimé squinted into the hot rain. "And I'll be glad to be done with the job. I can't say I like this part of South America. Mosquitos, chiggers, and *zancudos*. Ugh!"

Alexander swung his eyes to the shore. Like Aimé, he

would be glad to quit this savage land. Thick underbrush and bending palms crowded the banks of the Atabapo. The water, black as onyx, had sucked away the earth at the base of the trees, leaving their roots showing like giant, gnarled fingers. Close in to shore, alligators pushed their snouts up through a layer of yellow-green slime. Water snakes, most of them some fourteen feet long, swam up to the canoe, entwined themselves in the paddles, and terrified the Indians.

The canoe turned into the Temi a day later; it was a narrow, sluggish stretch of water. The air was motionless and hot and filled with the nervous humming of insects. From the Temi the canoe entered the Tuamini. Now the jungle came out over the black water and formed a patchwork roof that sagged in a tangle of vines and branches to the boat, and dropped spiders and snakes and rubbery worms onto the backs of the paddlers. And an Indian was stationed in the bow to hack a path with a machete through the always dripping, moss-covered branches. Once, the canoe found itself lodged between two submerged tree stumps. The pilot was almost forced to whip the Indians overside to free it. For a moment, there was in their eyes a murderous look for this man who demanded they enter water where the fourteen-foot-long snakes glided, silent and vicious.

At eleven o'clock in the morning of May 1st, the canoe sailed through a hot, roaring rain and, its bow making a long, sucking sound as it came up on the muddy bank, ran aground at the Mission of San Antonio de Yavita. Alexander and Aimé stepped ashore. They were thirty-three days out of San Fernando and three hundred miles distant from that spot.

The air was colored olive green. Mud and stick huts were scattered about the mission. The church itself loomed gaunt and tired above a low cloud of steam curling off the earth and drifting in from the jungle. Its walls were streaked and chipped, its timbers splintering wetly. An unpainted wooden cross stood aslant near its front door.

For a moment, as the explorers gazed round, the village seemed deserted. Only the sour stench of the jungle had life to it. Then flashes of brown were seen in doorless doorways here and there; and then the natives of the village were splashing toward them, surrounding them, plucking curiously at their clothing, and chattering words of welcome. Out of the mission came a tiny man in dark robes. Almost daintily, he gathered his skirts above the mud, revealing ankles as slender as young branches, and ran on tiptoes to the explorers. He held an umbrella but it seemed a useless contrivance. Tattered, it admitted more rain than it rejected. It was the pathetic comedy of civilization come too deep into the jungle.

The umbrella prodded a brown hip here and an elbow there as the little man made his way through the crowd of natives. When he came face-to-face with the newcomers he first blinked, then stared. His mouth dropped open and his eyes went as wide as a child's on Christmas morning. Water dribbled, unnoticed by him, from the tip of his stubby nose.

"It can't be! It can't be!" His voice, like his eyes, belonged to a child. It was high-pitched and excited. "White men . . . gentlemen! Here at my little jungle outpost!"

He suddenly went silent. An expression of suspicion crossed his pinched little face. His hand came forward, timidly and tentatively; a hand reaching for a mirage. Alexander gripped it. The touch of firm, real flesh released a fresh torrent of words from the tiny priest. They were real! He wasn't dreaming! They were real, quite real! And how happy he was to see them!

Father Hernando Comeso had been in the New World for fifteen years, ten of them at Yavita. Fifteen years away from Spain. Why he had not gone mad with homesickness, only the good and merciful Lord above knew. But he must not keep his fine visitors here in the rain. Where were his manners? Come along, come along up to the mission where there was a fire to dry their clothes and a sip of Spanish wine to soothe tired nerves and muscles. How are things at home? Is Bonaparte still on the march? Is it true that even his own people call him a butcher? His wonderful visitors—what a surprise it was to see them!—must tell him all the news. But, first, whatever possessed two such fine gentlemen to come to Yavita? Did they not agree that it was the end of the earth?

Before the open fire in the mission kitchen, the priest halted his flow of words long enough to listen, wide-eyed, to a description of the work that had brought Alexander and Aimé so deep into the jungle.

"Wonderful! Wonderful!" Father Comeso cried at the end of the recital. "A map of this country. It's just what we need. Perhaps it will bring more traders and settlers down here." He had been seated on a wooden stool and now he jumped to his feet. "I myself will arrange for your canoe to be dragged overland to the Pimichin. It will require many natives to do the job and—" he pressed clasped hands happily against his chest, "it will take three—no, at least four—days to complete the crossing. Almost a whole week for us to talk and talk and then talk some more. You have no idea how starved I am for the company of my own people and for news of home. I love my poor natives and I know I must do God's will, but—well, it is still very lonely. Here! Let me fill your glasses again."

He took them a short time later to engage men of the town for the portage. Twenty-three were hired. They carried the canoe from the water to a line of thick branches that would serve as rollers. A rope was attached to the bow.

A line of men took it to their shoulders and pulled the canoe forward. Others shoved at gunwales. One oldster, bandy-legged and toothless, hovered near the stern. As soon as one log was squeezed out from under the stern, he scooped it up, hurried to the bow, and set it down again. The rest of the time, serving as self-appointed foreman, he danced about and cackled orders to which not one of the workers paid the slightest attention.

Aimé, watching the canoe bump with agonizing slowness along a trail that disappeared into the jungle, massaged an unshaven jaw. "Four days to the Pimichin? More likely a lifetime."

Father Comeso's head ducked in and out among the streams of water pouring through the holes in his umbrella. "No, no! Just four days. And have no worry. I shall make the time pass quickly. I shall be the perfect host."

He proved to be as good as his word. He placed straw pallets in the kitchen for his guests. He heated water for their first real bath in weeks. He summoned native women to prepare the finest meal Yavita had to offer. And his jungle-wise eyes narrowed when he saw the explorers continually scratching the backs of their hands.

"You have pain and itching there, yes?"

Alexander nodded. "For two days now."

The priest waved the men to him. "Let me see."

They extended their hands, palms down. The skin about their knuckles was lined with whitish furrows. Father Comeso bent far over. A moment of squinting was followed by a very professional nod and an angry sigh. "I thought so. *Aradores*."

"*Aradores?*"

"The ploughmen. They are little insects that burrow under the skin. But have no fear. We will get rid of them. Maria will remove them."

Maria, summoned from her house, proved to be a mulatto woman who, from all she talked, might have had no more than ten words in her vocabulary. She glanced briefly, coldly, at the furrows, waved the explorers to a bench, heated a sharp wooden needle over a lamp, and sat down before Alexander. She took his hand and, without a single preliminary remark, drove the needle into one of the furrows. Alexander winced and choked back a cry of pain. The woman lifted unblinking eyes to his, challenging this white-faced visitor to remain silent as she probed again and again until she displayed an infinitesimal brown ball on the tip of the needle.

"*Arador,*" she announced gravely and immediately went in search of another.

Alexander called a halt to the operation near midnight. Close to ten of the little creatures had been plucked from his and Aimé's hands, leaving them swollen and bleeding. The mulatto woman promised to return with her needle the following day. As it turned out, her services were no longer required. An elderly Indian arrived just after dawn with a solution made from the branch of the *uzao* shrub. Into this bluish liquid the explorers plunged their hands. The aradores never bothered them again.

The travelers remained at Yavita for eight days. Each morning they went to watch the journey of the canoe to the Pimichin. They frowned worriedly at how it bumped over the rough log rollers and scraped against trees and bushes. Then they turned to the average workday of botanists and explorers. Threading their way through the dripping jungle, they took notes on the trees of the area—the laurels and ocoteas, the *Amasonia arboreas* and jacios, all rising through palms to heights of over one hundred feet. They added flowers and plants to their Europe-bound collection; they studied the deadly *mapanare* snake with its white belly and spotted back; they watched the Indians obtain a crude salt from the fruit of the palm tree called the *chimu;* they listened to stories of the tribes south across the Brazilian border who made a habit of eating their enemies and prisoners of war; and, of course, Alexander brought forth his sextant and established the geographical location of Yavita.

The canoe arrived at the Pimichin on the fourth of May. That was the day that Father Comeso's little face started to crumble. He pleaded, "You must not leave just yet. You want for nothing here. You have good food. You are safe from mosquitos." Knowing that years might pass before the lonely priest was visited by another white man, the explorers remained with him for another four days. Then, regretfully, he led them over the jungle trail to the Pimichin and the canoe, in which the new plant specimens were pushing the gunwales right down to the water.

Alexander and Aimé took their places at the stern. Father Comeso waded into the river to grip their hands for the last time. Tears glistened in his eyes and he kept them from rolling down his cheeks by sniffing repeatedly and wiggling his nose. He had spent all last night rehearsing memorable words of farewell, but all that now came forth were broken fragments of what was in his heart. "You have been so very good to me . . . I wish I could go with you . . . I know God will smile on your journey . . . I will say masses for you . . . Good-bye . . . I wish I could go with you . . . *Vaya con Dios.*"

He returned to shore, lifted his hand in blessing, then waved bravely as the canoe glided through the rain to midstream. Alexander and Aimé watched his tiny figure grow smaller until a bend in the river hid him from view. The last thing Alexander saw of him was a black tatter of umbrella fluttering desolately in the green air.

Four and a half hours and eighty-five bends in the Pimichin later, the canoe came out onto that tributary of the Amazon, the Río Negro.

South along the Río Negro the canoe sailed and Alexander regarded the land beyond the shore with awe. Such country he had never seen before. Thick jungles were broken by long, rolling prairies dotted with giant boulders. Circling in the distance were mountains that had been sliced into fantastic shapes by centuries of erosion. Alligators and boas were masters of the river. Jaguars, peccaries, tapirs, spiders, ants, and monkeys owned the shore. It was one of those spots in the world where man seemed to have no rightful place. It was as wild in this year 1800 as it had been at the beginning of time.

While he regarded the land with awe, Alexander viewed the weather with anger and alarm. When the rain wasn't falling fast and green, a suffocating mist obliterated the sky. The Casiquiare was fast approaching. He had traveled hundreds of miles—with, so it seemed to him, a dozen hardships per mile—to determine astronomically the location of that watery link between the Amazon and Orinoco systems. But such a determination required the sun and the stars, and he had not seen them for days. They were hiding somewhere above the infernal green mist. Without them, all the hardships of the past weeks would have gone in vain.

The pilot smiled at him and said comfortingly, "Have no fear, Señor. I have been here before. I promise you that, as soon as we leave these black waters, you will see the sun and the stars that eat away the clouds."

His words became fact. The sky began to clear just below the village of San Carlos, the southernmost point reached by the explorers. The sun came out—to be followed by brilliant stars at night—as the canoe, now close to the Brazilian border, swung into the Casiquiare and pointed its bow north, back up to the Orinoco.

They came ashore at the rock of Culimacari early in the evening. The air was thick and moist, but the Southern Cross lay white and motionless against a clear black sky.

"There you are!" Aimé cried as Alexander gently placed his sextant and chronometer on a flat rock. "The four most beautiful stars in the universe—ready and waiting for you!"

Alexander smiled briefly. "Just one of them—that's all I'll need," he said. There was a vacant quality to his voice. He really did not hear his own words. His mind was completely on the job at hand. He felt a thrust of excitement, the sort of excitement that can produce a nervous laugh. This was what he had traveled hundreds of miles for—a few minutes of silent and simple work.

He lifted the lid of the box containing the chronometer. He lowered his face to within inches of that large, intricate watch designed for determining longitude. He was more than just a little worried about the instrument. It had come rattling through rapids and bouncing over rough jungle trails. It had not been properly set for close to two years. From these two facts alone, he knew that its reading would not be exact. But, he told himself, it should be precise enough for the purposes of geography.

He watched the sweep second hand move gracefully and steadily from number to number. A faint sound of ticking came from within the instrument. Alexander consulted his watch, glanced again at the chronometer, scribbled briefly in his notebook, and said:

"69° 33′ 50″ longitude. But that's just a probability."

Aimé smiled and said loyally, "I'll wager it's a good probability."

"I hope so."

Alexander closed the lid of the box. Half the job was done.

Now he picked up the sextant. He carried it down to the river. He lifted it to his eye, aiming its telescope at a slender line of mercury in a small trough that Aimé placed close by; this was his "artificial horizon," replacing the rim of the sea during observations made on land. He adjusted the mirrors in the instrument until he saw in them the star *a* of the Southern Cross. Then, very slowly, he moved the vernier arm along its arc, bringing the star down to the line of mercury. The star, so bright to the naked eye, was dim, almost brown, in the darkened glass placed over the mirrors. It touched the silver-white line of mercury. Alexander held himself motionless, prolonging the kiss of star and mercury for a long moment. Then he took the instrument from his eye, turned it on its side, and squinted at the figure indicated on the vernier arc. He now had to take into consideration that the angle he had found between star and "artificial horizon" was exactly double an angle found on the actual horizon at sea. After a moment of rapid calculation in his notebook he turned to Aimé.

"2° 0′ 42″ north latitude."

He returned the sextant to its box and carried both sextant and chronometer to the canoe. Then he moved to Aimé, resting his back against a boulder, and sat down. He sighed. He shrugged. There was something almost comical in both the sound and the gesture. The job was done. After weeks of travel and pain, after miles on a half-dozen rivers, it was done. And it had taken so little time that it seemed to him that it was over before it had begun.

He stared up at the Southern Cross, so white against the black sky, and a feeling of defiance poured through him. Now let the mist come again. Let it hide those stars. Let it hide the sun. Let the rain fall in green sheets. He no longer cared what the weather decided to do. He had done his work, as best he could with his crude and weather-worn instruments. The hiding place of a small but very influential river was a hiding place no more. The Casiquiare was ready to take its place on the new maps of the world.

And *new* maps they would have to be. The old ones—the ones of legend and fantasy—would have to be scrapped. The makers of maps would no longer turn to fanciful tales of old to illustrate *how* and *where* two of the world's greatest river systems are connected. They would turn to the notebooks of Alexander von Humboldt.

Northwest, between high banks of granite and through hordes of mosquitos that once drove them to seek shelter beneath a waterfall, the travelers sailed, one taking magnetic and astronomical observations, the other collecting and classifying plants. Then, on May 21st, they clambered to the bow of the canoe. Dead ahead was a wide avenue of water. It stretched from east to west and crossed the Casiquiare. Into the eastern arm of that watery avenue the canoe swept and the travelers saw the settlement of Esmeralda over on the northern shore and heard the pilot shout from the tiller:

"It is the Orinoco!"

A long sigh escaped Alexander. He faced Aimé and his hand touched his friend's shoulder. He smiled, paying no attention to the stretching pain all along his cracked, swollen lips. The humidity, the shivering memory of slime-covered snakes, his ragged clothing—not one of these things was worth a moment's notice now. From now on the journey would be a journey home.

The words he had spoken so many weeks ago to Aimé at Cumaná came back to him.

"We'll collect plants—"

How they had lived up to that promise. Bundled aboard at present were thousands of plant specimens in triplicate, 1,400 of them already classified. Though the explorers watched the humidity destroy many of their number daily, they knew they would soon dispatch across the Atlantic many crates of plants hitherto unknown. Then would the eyes of Europe be opened to the wonders of South American vegetation.

"And we shall see the people—"

Ottomacs. Tamanacs. Gaujibos. Caribs. And a dozen other tribes. They had talked and lived with them all. Someday, upon their return to Europe, they would speak and write of these peoples. Kings and commoners alike would lose their disdain of the South American Indian. They would learn that he was primitive, yes; often savage, yes; always superstitious, yes; but not stupid. He had his own traditions, many of them similar to those of the white man. He had his customs of living and his ways of supporting his family and himself. He was primitive, but capable of taking his rightful place in the new and growing South America.

"And we'll see the land—"

Not only had they seen the land, but they had mapped it, pointing out numerous inland stations, missions, islands, waterfalls, mountains, and jungles. Such maps would light the way for future explorations and emigration.

"And we'll determine the connection between the Orinoco and Amazon systems—"

There was no need for Alexander to dwell on the importance to future map-making of that determination. What now occupied his mind was the fact that a country nine times the size of the kingdom of Spain had been shown to be navigable in all directions. Such knowledge could effect great changes in the economic and social life of eastern

South America. Settlers could move deep into the interior; trade goods could be brought in and out; the Indians themselves, putting the river connection to greater use, could overcome their hatred of distant tribes by getting to know those tribes. The connected river systems could help to unify South America and make it ready for the civilization advancing yearly upon its shores.

Alexander leaned back against the gunwale. Again he sighed deeply. Yes, it was time to go home. "Home" in this case was Angostura, far to the north near the mouth of the Orinoco. There, he and Aimé would plan new adventures.

Angostura.

Place of 6,000 souls, black and white, lying inland 240 miles from the mouth of the Orinoco. Place one day to be called Cuidad Bolívar after the South American liberator. Place of lofty stone houses built atop black rocks. Place of stagnant pools and narrow, busy streets running parallel with the river. Place of many boats at the *embarcadero,* of traders, merchants, doctors, priests, soldiers, and scholars. In other words, a city, not a mere settlement.

It should have been a haven of peace and rest for Alexander after 1,725 miles on the Orinoco and after twenty days spent coming downriver from Esmeralda. But in the light of his experiences there, he remembered it as a place of dread.

Just south of Angostura, a sickness of the jungle—typhoid—crept upon the two men and gripped them. It began with a feeling of listlessness, a lethargy that made any effort at work a torture. Then, as they lay beneath the palm-leaf roof of their little toldo, the fever enveloped them, followed by chills and then more fever. Alexander, though the smaller and more frail of the two, managed to cure himself by drinking a concoction of honey and the extract from the angostura tree.

But the mixture had no effect on Aimé. He vomited it over the side of the canoe, then fell back among his bundles of precious plant specimens, his head lolling in pain, his cheeks gray beneath their tan, his forehead coated with perspiration. After watching him a few moments, the pilot beckoned Alexander to the stern. His expression was grave.

"You must know the truth of these things, Señor," he said softly and gently. "I have seen many men sick with the fever. When they cannot keep down the angostura bark, it often means death."

Alexander, still weak himself, felt a shiver run through his body. He gripped the roof of the cabin to support himself. His knuckles were dead white. He heard his own voice, distant and hoarse.

"Nothing must happen to him. Nothing! He must hold on. There will be a doctor at Angostura." He felt his voice rising, slipping away from him. "The doctor will make him well. You will see. You will see."

The pilot met his eyes. His face was expressionless. He said, tonelessly, "Yes. If the Señor says so."

The doctor they found at Angostura was Felix Fafreras. His house was in a cool valley eighteen miles out of the city. Aimé was taken there and placed in a bed in a high ceilinged room. A servant was sent to the mission at Carony for bark from the angostura tree. Aimé received infusions of quinine. He gagged and threw them up. At last, his head fell back against the pillow and he slept.

Dr. Fafreras drew Alexander into the hall. "There is nothing we can do until the angostura bark arrives. We can only wait and pray. You had best rest yourself. You do not look too well yourself. Your room is at the end of the hall."

But worry made rest impossible for Alexander. He could

not just lie on a soft bed while his friend hovered near death in a room so close that he could hear him moaning. He had to do something to fill the hours and his mind lest he go mad. He called for Dr. Fafreras' carriage and rode into Angostura, directing the driver to take him down to the dock.

The canoe was still there in the water, riding oddly high and lopsided now that its cargo had been placed in a warehouse on the dock. Alexander entered the warehouse. The pilot and his paddlers sat guard near the bundles of plant specimens. Along the far wall were the cages containing the animals captured on the Orinoco. Alexander stared dully at this little zoo of two manikin birds, spider monkeys, marmosets, two guans, a motmot, and two night-loving monkeys. In the last cage was a small furry monkey with the face of a very funny old man. One day Alexander would be called the discoverer of this little creature. It would be known as "Humboldt's woolly monkey."

But who cared about discoveries this night? And who cared about the bundles of plant specimens stacked so neatly there at the center of the warehouse? What were discoveries in trade for a friend's life? What good had all the work of Lofting done that great botanist? The jungles of South America had killed him. Those jungles had killed so many good men of foreign lands—from priests to Spanish soldiers to explorers to scientists. . . .

Alexander left the warehouse quickly. Then he walked aimlessly through the town, seeing nothing. A hundred memories of Aimé flashed across the picture frame of his mind. There was Aimé, so long ago in France, ready and willing to travel anywhere at a moment's notice. There was Aimé, grinning and panting at his side atop Tenerife and staring like a child out over the beckoning Atlantic.

There was Aimé cursing softly as he watched the humidity on the Orinoco destroy so many of his precious plant specimens. And there was Aimé that terrible day back on the Apure when the swirling river water had almost swamped the lancha, Aimé standing at his side with the wind whipping his hair and the rain lashing his face as he shouted, "On my back, Alex! On my back! I'll swim us to shore!" And then there was Aimé grinning happily, almost foolishly, after the lancha, managing to stay afloat, had put the rough water behind them.

Alexander stopped suddenly on a muddy street. Oblivious of the traffic about him, he lifted his eyes to the star-flecked sky. To that sky he called silently, "To whatever force is up there behind your stars—the God of the white man, the Cachimona of the Indians—please save Aimé. Let Bonpland live. Let him work again. Let him travel again and see all the things he wants to see. . . ."

Alexander lowered his head, suddenly conscious of passing black eyes staring curiously at him. He unclenched his hands and found that his nails had dug arcing furrows into his palms. He returned swiftly to Dr. Fafreras' carriage and rode back to the tall house in the valley.

Back in his room, he could not sleep. He lighted a lamp and tried to write a little. There were so many letters to be sent back to Europe—to his brother, his friends, his old teachers. But the quill pen refused to move, refused to fashion a single word. Alexander stared dully at the blank sheet of paper.

He was sitting with the pen motionless in his hand when an Indian servant burst into the room. The crash of the door flying open turned the explorer swiftly in his chair. He felt himself go white when he saw the native's expression. In the split second that the two men stared at each other before the native spoke, Alexander knew what the man was going to say.

"Come quick, Señor! Your friend is dead!"

Alexander's chair went over on its back. He didn't know until later that he had flung the pen halfway across the room. But he knew he was making a low groaning sound in his throat as he pushed his way past the native and ran down the hall and into Aimé's room. Staring, he stopped at the foot of the bed. Aimé's head was turned to the side on the pillow. His eyes were closed, the lids looking slightly purplish. His lips hung slack. His great chest was still beneath the blankets. The low groaning sound came up out of Alexander's throat and emerged a thin, anguished cry. He moved around the foot of the bed, threw back the covers, and grabbed Aimé's wrist, searching for a pulse beat. All he could feel was the pounding of the blood in his own temples.

Then he felt himself being brushed aside. He almost lost his balance. He blinked and then saw that Dr. Fafreras, his pointed beard sharply black against his white nightshirt, had taken his place at the bedside. Fafreras had Aimé's wrist between his fingers. He held it for a long moment, then released it and placed his hand over the Frenchman's heart. He replaced the covers gently. His face was crimson, hard with anger, but his voice was apologetic.

"I'm sorry you have been put to this trouble, Señor. Your friend is not dead. He is in a coma."

Alexander started to speak. Words wouldn't come. He shook his head. He was certain he hadn't heard the doctor correctly.

"Not dead? A coma?"

"Yes. A very deep coma." Fafreras glared at the native trembling in the doorway. "I placed this poor, stupid wretch here to watch him. He mistook the coma for death."

Alexander digested these facts slowly. His legs were still watery, but now he wanted to laugh—the shivering, uncontrollable laugh of relief. He was filled suddenly, strangely, with the conviction that Aimé was now safe from the typhoid. It would not claim his life. He had no real reason for knowing this. He only knew that he *knew* it. Perhaps the conviction came from the fact that he felt it impossible that he should have to live again through the fear and anguish he had experienced in these past few minutes. Oh, hang the reasons! He *knew* Aimé was safe. That was enough for him.

He pressed the native's arm as he moved through the doorway and said over his shoulder to Dr. Fafreras, "Do not be hard on him. I, too, was fooled. I too thought it was death."

He returned to his room and, still fully dressed, threw himself across the bed. He immediately fell into a deep sleep.

The bark of the angostura tree arrived the following day. It was mixed with honey and fed to Aimé. The botanist hovered on the edge of the coma for another day. Then, late in the afternoon, Alexander entered the Frenchman's room and found him awake. He was pale and weak, but smiling.

"I seem to have been on a journey all my own these past few days, my friend. I'm glad that you did not have to accompany me."

Strength flowed back into the botanist all during the remainder of the week. The color came back into his face. His eyes regained their old luster. By Saturday, he was sitting up in bed. He was clean shaven and worrying about a bit of food—"Please, no fish and plantains"—and asking about his plants. In other words, he was firmly set on the road to recovery.

It was then that the two men began to talk about the future, a future that looked as fresh as the golden dawn after the blackness of a stormy night. Where should they go next? That was the question that threaded its exciting way through their every discussion.

Where to now? The western face of South America with its mountains and jungles and grand traditions of the Incas and Mayans? Central America, thin and swampy neck of land separating the Caribbean from the Pacific? Mexico? What about Cuba?

Cuba?

They tasted the word. It sounded fine. They had missed it on the trip out from Spain because of illness—the very same illness that had just gripped Aimé—aboard the *Pizarro*. Cuba was Spain's most important possession in the New World and its major city, Havana, was one of the busiest ports on this side of the Atlantic.

And from there the explorers could travel to North America. Suddenly, the fragrance of pines was in their nostrils. North America it would be. They would move up through the land of the Revolution to the deep, silent forests and blue lakes of Canada and then back down the Ohio and Mississippi rivers to New Orleans. Then west to Panama to study the possibility of a canal to link the Caribbean with the Pacific. And then still further west, possibly to the Philippines; possibly around the world.

Aimé threw back the covers with true French impetuosity. "I think it is time to be getting up."

Alexander placed a restraining hand against his friend's shoulder. "Not just yet. You have a long road to full recovery ahead of you. And we have much work yet to do with your collections and my notes. It is now June. We'll work here until late autumn. Then we'll go up to Cumaná and search out a ship for Cuba. We should be in Havana before Christmas!"

CHAPTER EIGHT

Havana

November 24, 1801

Sailed for Cuba this day . . . Ship small and uncomfortable . . . Evening cool.

November 26, 1801

Sea covered with a bluish film, quite beautiful . . . Hauled some aboard and examined it in the microscope . . . It appeared to be formed of an innumerable quantity of filaments . . . Could be vestiges of the eggs of mollusca . . . Could be fragments of fuci.

November 30, 1801

Foul weather today . . . Wind hard to N.N.E. . . A darkish blue tint observable on the sky . . . Ship rolled badly . . . We saw, amidst the dashing of the waves, two seas crossing each other, one from the north, the other from N.N.E. . . Waterspouts formed a mile distant . . . Deck caught fire owing to carelessness of American cook . . . soon extinguished.

December 3, 1801

Uneasy at the approach of a small vessel . . . Captain thought it a pirate ship . . . It turned out to be the *Balandra del Frayle*—"the sloop of the Monk" . . . the monk is a rich Franciscan who engages in trade with the Danish islands.

December 9, 1801

Weather miserable for five days now . . . Wind hard . . . Rain . . . Ship rolling badly.

December 18, 1801

Sailing close in to the coast of Cuba, three miles out from Cape San Antonio . . . Delicious aromatic odor coming to us from shore . . . Sailors claim this odor not perceived when approaching from Mexico.

December 19, 1801

Landed this day at Havana after a passage of twenty-five days in continuous bad weather . . . City beautiful as seen from ship . . . On entering port, you pass between the fortress of the Morro and the fort of San Salvador de la Punta . . . You then pass along a narrow channel until you enter a large bay . . . Havana itself is to your right, walled for defense . . . Outside the walls are the suburbs of the Horcon, Jesu-Maria, Guadaloupe, and Señor de la Salud . . . Vegetation appears rich and graceful . . . After passing the wrecks of several vessels sunk in the shoals, we dropped anchor.

Such were ALEXANDER'S NOTES on his journey from the coast of Venezuela to Havana.

His opinion of the beauty of the city changed as soon as he and Aimé stepped ashore. They entered the carriage of Señor Cuesta, the distinguished businessman who was to be their host during the next weeks, and immediately found themselves lost in a labyrinth of narrow, winding, unpaved streets. Mud came up to the knees of pedestrians and the storekeepers who hawked their wares in front of unpainted stalls. Flat-faced adobe buildings, once white but now streaked and graying, seemed to lean out over the thoroughfares, leaving only a narrow strip of leaden sky showing overhead. Women chattered to each other from high, narrow windows and unconcernedly threw their cooking slops down atop the passers-by. Children, half-naked and screaming, ran dangerously close to the wheels of the carriage. At every step, beggars approached with that attitude of sly humility that was the mark of their profession. Garbage was piled high in open doorways. To its stench was added the choking odor of salted meat.

Señor Cuesta, bearded and always dignified, held a handkerchief delicately to his nose. "Our streets—they are a terrible cross that we must bear. It is very difficult and expensive to bring stones all the way from Vera Cruz. I will show you where we have tried to pave with the trunks of mahogany trees."

The carriage turned into the Avenida de Paula and suddenly beauty replaced filth and squalor; the air grew cool, as if relieved to be away from the mud and stench. Here was a fine public walk where officers from the Morro and San Salvador fortresses and the headquarters of the Commandant of Marines walked with their ladies. Here, after sundown, the caleches and volantes of the wealthy and the aristocratic rolled past each other at a stately clip and the occupants of one nodded to the occupants of another with quiet, long practiced dignity. Here in spacious parks the velvet-and-lace clad children of the officials of the Correo or General Post Office, the Factory of Tobacco, and the various foreign legations played under the watchful eyes of pretty and not-so-pretty governesses. In the distance was the hospital of Santa Paula, the Botanical Garden over near the Campo de Marte, and the cathedral of Havana.

Señor Cuesta called the carriage to a halt before the cathedral. Inside, Aimé read aloud the inscription over the tomb of Christopher Columbus.

> "Oh relics and image of the great Colón
> A thousand ages are encompassed in thy Urn
> And in the memory of our Nation."

Quietly, Señor Cuesta explained, "His ashes were brought to this church only recently from San Domingo. They were interred here in the same year that the ashes of Hernando Cortés were transferred from one church to another in Mexico. It is an interesting coincidence, is it not, that, in the very same year, the remains of the two greatest men in the conquest of the New World should find their way to new resting places?"

In the weeks that followed, Alexander's life came to be composed of three elements—work, play, and hatred.

The work occupied all the daylight hours—and many of those of the nights—of January and February, 1802. He surveyed the vicinity of Havana and the plains of Guines. He discovered that the recorded longitude of Havana was more than one fifth of a degree in error. The position of this port, so vital militarily and commercially to Spain, had been fixed at 5° 38′ 11″. With Captain Don Dionisio Galeano, who had surveyed the Straits of Magellan, he made observations on a series of eclipses of the satellites of Jupiter and enabled Havana to find its way at last to its correct position on the maps of the world.

He followed this accomplishment with a trip into the interior of Cuba. He visited indigo, tobacco, and cotton plantations; he studied the minerals of the island; he traveled along its rivers and spoke with its people, rich and poor alike. The notes made on this trip were later turned into his *Political Essay on the Island of Cuba,* a work that did much to acquaint the Old World with the natural resources, geography, industry, and customs of this fabulous island in the New.

The cool evenings brought the moments of play. He and Aimé were entertained night after night in the homes of the great families of the city. Everyone from the youngest to the oldest in those homes was eager for and fascinated by firsthand news from Europe. No one seemed disturbed by the fact that the travelers had been on the western side of the Atlantic for close to two years.

And the hatred?

The hatred had begun back at Cumaná, months ago, when Alexander had visited a slave market and had watched a group of frightened Africans placed on sale before a horde of cigar smoking, perfumed plantation owners. In a cold fury, he had written his brother, Wilhelm, "The slaves exposed for sale were young men from fifteen to twenty years of age. Every morning coconut oil was distributed among them, with which they rubbed their bodies to give them a black polish. The people who came to purchase examined the teeth of these slaves, to judge their age and health, forcing their mouths open as we do with horses in a market."

Now the hatred was in him again. It rose hot and molten from deep within him and filled his mouth with the yellow taste of brass whenever he passed the barracoon down near the waterfront. Let him come within a hundred yards of that place, let the first whiff of the stink of all the thousands of sweating, filth-encrusted bodies that had passed through it clog his nostrils, and then see what happened to everything he would see or had seen that day; the velvet-and-lace children at play with their hoops and balls in the park by the Avenida de Paula, the cathedral thrusting magnificent spires against an azure sky, that ship that had stood with all sails spread between the Morro and San Salvador at dawn—all these things, every last one of them, right down to the tiniest child with the puffiest cheeks, suddenly became foul and ugly in his mind with the first wave of stench from the barracoon.

It was here, to the barracoon with its barracks and great inner courtyard, that the black men and women and children of Africa were directly brought in chains from the hundreds of slavers that yearly made port at Havana. They were hauled here in carts or run through the streets in the early morning. The half-naked children who had screamed at Señor Cuesta's carriage now shouted obscenities and threw gobs of mud at them; the beggars sniggered and felt very superior to them; through the years, they were an endless parade of black Christs, each on his way to his own personal Calvary. Still sick from the airless holds of the slavers and the lack of food, more of them stumbled than ran. All along the line there would be cries of pain as, one after another, they dropped, the sudden pulling taut of chains causing wrist and leg irons to bite into skin already rubbed to shining, pink rawness.

They were herded into the inner courtyard of the barracoon. They were doused with water to cleanse away the filth of the ship and of themselves that had collected on their bodies since Africa. They were fed sun-dried meat, pumpkins, batatas, and maize to get them back on their feet. Coconut oil, as in Cumaná, was passed among them and they coated their bodies with it. Then they were marched out to the front of the barracoon and ranged along the wall in a long, trembling, evil-smelling line before the buyers.

Filth. Pain. Cruelty. Misery. Shame. All these words and all the foulest words man can devise—work them all into one sickening word and, for Alexander, it would spell slavery. He could not look at the barracoon; he would deliberately walk out of his way to avoid it. He could not watch a slaver, low in the water as it slid up to dockside, without wanting to see it at the bottom of the ocean. But when he spoke out against the barracoon and all it represented, when he said such things as, "No country can hope to be great until all its people are free," his hosts in the great houses of the city regarded him with the patient smiles usually reserved for children.

"How can you say that, my friend?" one of them asked one evening at dinner. "The greatest slave trader the world has seen is England. She also happens to be one of the world's greatest powers. Even we Spanish are forced to admit that fact."

"Yes. But she has been trying to abolish slave trading for years. She will put an end to it. Very soon—"

His host rested his elbows on the table. "You know, there are two sides to the coin of slavery here in the colonies. We Spanish, particularly here in Cuba, are not as cruel as you might think. Floggings are the rarity rather than the rule. The slave is given the chance to earn his freedom. He is not separated from his family—"

"But his ears are cut off or his eyes gouged out if he tries to escape."

"Unfortunately, yes. But only by a few of the owners." The host now eyed Alexander quizzically. "Tell me, my friend, you are one of us, are you not?"

"I don't understand your question."

"Your title is 'Baron'?"

"Yes."

"Then you are of the nobility. As are we. And you surely must know, as do we, that some men on this earth are meant by God to serve and others to be served."

"Such would seem to be the case." Alexander held his wine glass in stiff fingers. He was white at the temples and the whiteness was spreading down to his cheeks. "But if

God intended the servants to serve in slavery, then He is not God at all, but the Devil."

His host laughed an easy laugh that was meant to change a subject not suitable for a table spread with fine lace and delicate china. "You have quite a way with words, Baron. Someday you must tell me why you sympathize so deeply with the slaves. It is a strange sympathy for one of the nobility."

Perhaps it was, Alexander thought. It was the sort of sympathy that was ordinarily born of personal pain. But he had never known the ache of poverty. He had never known the heartbreak of being forcibly carried from his homeland. He had never known the horror of chains and poverty. But the sympathy was there, just the same. It had been there, a living, pulsing thing at the core of his being, for years. He had first recognized it in the Beyreuth and Fichtel mountains when he had fought for better working conditions for the miners.

Now that sympathy forced him to fight against slavery. His only weapons were to be his brain and his pen. But they were to prove adequate weapons indeed.

He visited the government offices at Havana and began to piece together the horrible story of slavery in the New World. It had started, he learned, in 1494 when Columbus had sent back to Spain for sale as slaves five hundred Indians he had captured; but Queen Isabella, questioning the manner in which they had been captured, had ordered them returned to their homeland. Slavery then had to wait for a real foothold in the Western Hemisphere until 1503, when King Ferdinand ordered a number of African Negroes sent to the newly founded colony of Haiti.

In the years that followed, the growth of the slave trade had run parallel with the growth of the New World. The English, the French, the Danes, and the Portuguese had all profited from this traffic in human beings. In one of the government houses, a clerk flipped open a ledger, cleared his throat, and said in a dry, impersonal voice, "Here are the figures on the number of slaves imported into the New World in 1790. By the British: 38,000. By the French: 20,000. The Portuguese: 10,000. The Dutch: 4,000. The Danes: 2,000. Total: 74,000."

And there were other, even more staggering figures to be gathered. Between 1680 and 1786, the British alone had shipped to their American and West Indian possessions 2,130,000 Africans, roughly 20,000 a year. Out of every one hundred Negroes carried westward, approximately seventeen died en route or were thrown overboard as damaged merchandise. So many others perished in harbor or while being broken into their labors that not more than fifty of the original hundred survived to work effectively for their new masters.

Alexander's trip into the interior of Cuba netted him more information on both the rights and treatment of slaves. From one plantation owner, he first heard the term *buscar amo.* "It is one of his rights, Señor. Let us say the slave has a complaint against his master. He may leave that master if he finds another willing to buy him."

After that, the question with which so many Negroes approached him on the island made sense. The question was "Quiere usted comprarme?" It meant, "Will you buy me, sir?"

The plantation owner went on to list other rights, some of which had been mentioned that night at dinner. "He may not only work for his freedom, but he may also marry according to his own inclination. And he may acquire property to pay for the freedom of his wife and children."

But the code of slavery failed to embrace other vital points. It did not limit the punishment given a slave; nor did it specify the duration of his day's labor; nor the type of food and care he was to be given.

And his rights were as nothing compared to those of his owner. The owner had the privilege of viewing him either as a short term investment, refusing to safeguard his health and working him to death quickly, or as a long term investment, spending money on proper food and housing for him in the hope of profiting from his labors over a span of many years. If a runaway was captured, the master could punish him as he saw fit. If it was deemed necessary, a slave could be branded for purposes of identification; the customary method was to clip the ear; in fairness, it must be said that this practice was limited to very few areas.

The story of slavery in the New World so revolted Alexander that he did not stop his inquiry into it upon his departure from Cuba; in fact, he did not stop even after he had left South America for good. The years saw him collecting all sorts of data, from statistics that dealt with figures in the thousands to individual illustrations of man's inhumanity to man. In the latter category, the statement of a witness before a British investigation into slavery in 1789 always left him speechless with anger. "If the slaves are whipped," the witness had said, "to make them dance on the deck of a slaveship—if they are forced to sing in chorus 'messe, messe, mackerida' (how gaily we live among the whites)—this only proves the care we take of the health of these men."

All the facts of the story of slavery, from the long rolls of statistics to the smallest story, became "Cuba and the Slave Trade," one of the most stirring chapters in his *Political Essay on the Island of Cuba.* These same facts were used time and again throughout his life in anti-slavery speeches delivered before political congresses. His views that slavery should be abolished in both North and South America, that all men should be free, and that nations would find their true greatness in the freedom of their people so impressed Simón Bolívar that the great liberator of South America credited Alexander with inspiring him to the Second American Revolution.

In March, 1801, Alexander and Aimé's work in Cuba was completed. Their minds focused on the next step in their travels and they found they were confronted by two equally engaging possibilities. They could book passage northward to the United States or they could join the squadron of Admiral Ariztizabel for a journey to Mexico.

While they were trying to choose between the two, an aging Paris newspaper arrived among their mail from Europe. It drove all thoughts of Mexico and the United States from mind.

"Listen to this!" Aimé shouted, pointing to a column in the paper. "Captain Charles Baudin departed this day from France to circumnavigate the globe. His exploration of the oceans of the world had been delayed close to four years. The Captain will sail around Cape Horn and touch the Peruvian coast within a year. . . ."

Alexander grabbed the paper. "It's dated several months ago. That means Baudin should arrive in Peru very shortly. I'll wager he'll put in at Lima. He was always talking about that port. It's the natural one for him to choose."

Aimé regarded his friend closely. "We're both thinking the same thing, aren't we?—that we should join Baudin at Lima."

"Yes," Alexander said. "I had very much looked forward to going with him when the voyage was first planned. I think the greatest disappointment of my life came when Bonaparte cancelled it."

"And mine, too."

"You're willing to give up North America and Mexico to try to meet him at Lima?"

"Of course. It's our chance to sail around the world. That sort of opportunity doesn't come to many."

"Then it's settled," Alexander said happily. "We'll engage passage for South America immediately. With luck, we should arrive in Lima long before Baudin."

Aimé, suddenly cautious, pursed his lips. "But suppose he doesn't put in at Lima?"

Alexander was ready with the only possible answer. "That's a chance we'll have to take."

"And suppose he won't take us aboard? Suppose he hasn't space for us?"

"That's another chance we'll have to take. If I know Baudin, he'll *make* space for us."

And so the decision was made and the two men prepared to leave Cuba. They divided their plant specimens, collected in triplicate, in three identical parts. One was placed aboard a ship bound for France via Cadiz; another went aboard a vessel headed for England, whence it would be dispatched for Germany; the third was designated to remain in Havana for the time being. In this way, they were certain that at least one shipment would survive the hazards of the Atlantic crossing. It was a precaution well taken. The ship on the Cadiz run went down off the coast of Africa.

Alexander, unable to book passage on a large vessel, hired a forty-ton sloop for the first step of their journey to meet Baudin, the voyage across the Caribbean to the port of Cartagena on the northwest coast of Colombia.

They went aboard the sloop on March 9, 1801. It raised sail and moved down the channel and past the Morro and the fort of San Salvador. The helmsman swung the wheel over and the little ship faced southwest. At the end of twenty-one days, it would arrive in Cartagena. The explorers would be again on South American soil.

CHAPTER NINE

The Harmony and Chimborazo

THEIR WELCOME to Cartagena was a fearsome one.

The sloop stood a mile out from the harbor entrance late in the day of Palm Sunday, March 30, 1801. The sky was sullen, the sea wild, the wind fierce and coming over the bow from starboard.

Waves rolled in under the little ship, lifted it high, and then lunged away from beneath it with savage delight, leaving it to crash down into deep green chasms rimmed by a frosting of hissing spray. Water plunged inboard from all sides. It chopped down over the bow and threw the legs of a seaman out from under him and dumped him screaming up against the cabin wall. It broke over the deck in dissolving walls and left the mainmast shivering and the rigging hazy in a frenzied dance.

The seaman who had been thrown against the cabin was hauled to his feet by a fellow crewman. Stumbling against the lurch and roll of the ship, the two men made their way to the mainmast and clung to it, as if afraid ever to move again.

All this Alexander saw from the stern. His grip on the starboard rail was firm. Directly behind him stood Aimé. To his left, the Captain gripped the wheel; the man's face was a chalky mask of anger as he squinted into the wind; the heaving of his chest was in perfect rhythm with the heaving of the deck; he and his sloop had become one.

Between the rising mountains of water, Alexander saw the Colombian coast. He would glimpse a stretch of palm forest and then up would come a wave of green and then it would sweep away and he would catch sight of long, low cliffs against the gray sky with its grayer clouds running hard for the sea and then the water would be there again, mounting to burst in a cloud of spray or tumble down on the ship.

He heard the Captain shout in the same instant he saw the worst of such waves hurl itself at the ship. It came, high and rolling, from the starboard. It seemed to hang motionless above the sloop for a split second, reveling in its towering might and disdainful of its little victim, before it toppled down amidships. The seamen at the mast disappeared from view. Alexander felt the vessel stagger from bow to stern, as if broken in two. There was the scrape and howl of wood grinding against metal; the scream of ropes stretched to the breaking point; and, most frightening of all, the harsh crackle and sickening pop, like bones breaking somewhere inside, of sailcloth ripping and then pulling free of its lines. The ship heeled far over. Alexander felt his feet go out from under him. He held onto the rail with animal savagery. The deck continued to go over on its side until he was no longer standing but hanging from the rail, with his knees and the tips of his shoes banging against the planking.

Instinctively, he had clamped his eyes shut as the wave had crashed inboard. Now he opened them again. The wave was gone, but he beheld a world madder than the one he had shut from view a moment ago. The seamen at the mainmast had not been washed away. Their arms were still locked about the dripping wood and their faces were pressed hard against it and they were choking and screaming all at the same time, water gushing from their mouths; but their bodies were thigh deep in the sea. The ship had been smashed over almost on her beam end. Another wave would send her all the way over; water would pour through her hatches and she would head straight for the bottom. Forward of the mainmast, a length of sailcloth was snapping viciously in the wind.

Alexander twisted his body half around and, with one elbow hooked over the rail, grabbed Aimé's arm. The Frenchman's face was dead white. His lips were moving in silent prayer. The men stared at each other, each frozen with the same thought. This was the end of their journey. This was the end of their work together. This was the end of every journey and of all work. Suddenly and a little crazily, Alexander remembered Aimé's attack of typhoid fever. It was silly—silly and stupid—that a man should survive such an illness to die in this way. . . .

The Captain's voice reached him above the shriek of the wind and the groan of the slanting ship. "That sail! That stay-sl! Cut it away! Cut it away!"

The words melted Alexander's frozen muscles. He obeyed the command immediately, with all the instinctive discipline life shows when it is trying to stay alive. He released his hold on the rail and flung himself forward and downward to the main cabin. He paused, a knot of sodden, aching flesh, against the cabin wall and stared at the whipping sailcloth up forward. He was not a sailor, but he recognized the terrible danger of that dancing triangle of canvas to the ship. It was the staysail, and its sheet had parted at the clew.

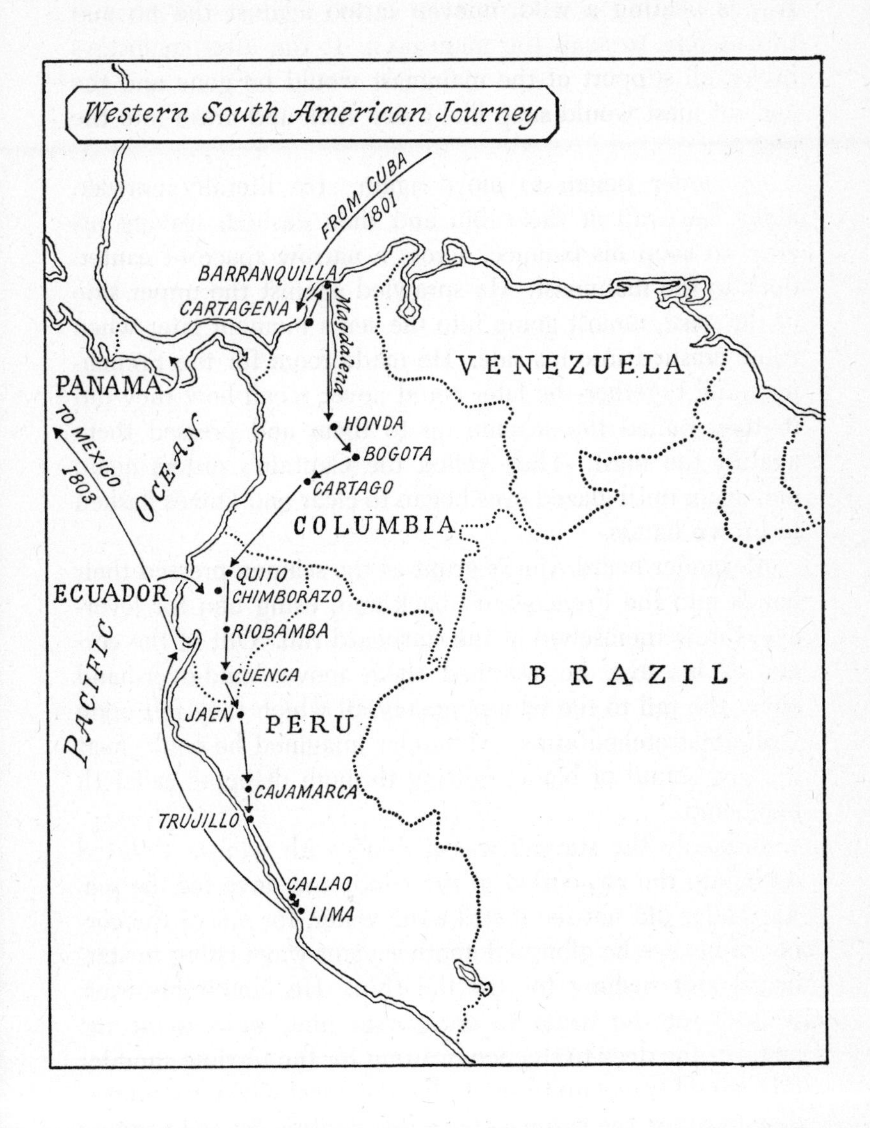
Western South American Journey
FROM CUBA
1801
BARRANQUILLA
CARTAGENA
Magdalena
VENEZUELA
PANAMA
TO MEXICO
1803
OCEAN
HONDA
BOGOTA
CARTAGO
COLUMBIA
QUITO
ECUADOR
CHIMBORAZO
RIOBAMBA
CUENCA
BRAZIL
JAEN
PERU
PACIFIC
CAJAMARCA
TRUJILLO
CALLAO
LIMA

It was beating a wild, uneven tattoo against the jib and threatening to snap the mainstays. If the after mainstays broke, all support of the mainmast would be gone and the ancient mast would snap like a dry stick and crash into the sea. . . .

Alexander began to move again. He literally crawled along the wall of the cabin and then dashed, waving his arms to keep his balance, across a narrow space of canted deck to the mainmast. He sprawled against the upper side of the mast, almost going into the sea a moment later when Aimé crashed into his side. He made room for the Frenchman and together—he later could never recall how they did it—they pulled the seamen up to them and pressed them against the mast. They yelled the Captain's orders again and again until glazed eyes began to clear and knives flashed in brown hands.

Alexander heard Aimé's grunt as the seamen pressed their hands into the Frenchman's back and, using him for leverage, threw themselves at the starboard rail. Out of the corner of his eye, he watched them move hand-over-hand along the rail to the whipping staysail which they fell upon with outstretched arms. Alexander imagined he could hear the raw sound of blades cutting through dripping sailcloth and hemp.

Suddenly the staysail was a thing with wings. It lifted itself into the air, curled in the wind, and dove for the sea. Alexander did not see it strike the water, for out of the corner of his eye he glimpsed another giant wave rising to starboard and rushing toward the ship. He closed his eyes, waiting for the water to crash over him, waiting for the angle of the deck to steepen, waiting for the terrible shudder that would travel up through the mainmast when it slammed down against the surface of the sea, waiting for the gagging death that must follow that shudder. All the work to save the mainmast had been in vain. It would hit the sea and its canvas, like a great saucer, would fill with water, and the sloop would go under—forever.

A watery explosion sounded behind him. He continued to wait for the water. But it did not come. Instead, the deck began to swing wildly, sickeningly, underfoot. He did not have the presence of mind to realize that there was something very wonderful about the swinging of that deck.

His mind began to clear, and he wondered, almost impatiently, what had become of the wave. He forced his eyes open. He was still clinging to the mainmast; his arms were wrapped about it and his fingers, like claws, had scraped deep ridges in the wet wood. He turned his head cautiously to peer at Aimé, still pressed against his back.

While staring at Aimé, he realized the angle of the deck had changed. It was level! No, it couldn't be! But it was! As level as a deck could be in an angry sea. He looked beyond the Frenchman and saw that the giant wave had disappeared. Only later did he come to reason that the wave had crested and broken before reaching the ship. It had rolled down into a trough of the sea, passed under the ship, and wrenched it upright.

But for the present, his mind, still fuzzy with shock, had only room for the understanding that he and Aimé were still alive. It was a delicious understanding that gently pulled his legs out from under him. He twisted his body as he fell so that he ended up sitting against the mast, his head lolling on one shoulder in exhaustion. Aimé sank down at his side.

When the Frenchman had the strength to speak, he said, "I hope Baudin appreciates us. We are certainly going to a great deal of trouble for him."

The ship took shelter in a cove above the harbor entrance that night. The next day, in better weather, it sailed into Cartagena.

Alexander scribbled in his notebook:

"Cartagena to Hondo.
"Hondo to Bogota.
"Bogota to Quito.
"Quito to Lima."

He sat back and smiled at the almost illegible words. Twelve words. An outline of his journey down the western face of South America to Captain Charles Baudin. There on paper, the trip looked so simple. In truth, the words represented some 2,000 miles of jungles and mountains and twisting rivers.

He and Aimé remained in Cartagena just a few days. Then they moved inland and placed their equipment aboard a *bongo,* a large dugout, and paddled out into the yellow waters of the Río Magdalena. For fifty-five days they remained on that river, following its sluggish course southward across the face of Colombia. Palm forests crowded the banks. Egrets and parrots rose screaming from the trees. Alligators dozed by the hundreds in the hot sunlight. The air was thick and moist. This was the land of the Orinoco all over again.

The jungle fell behind them at the small, tumbledown village of Hondo. They now stood on rising ground, rising ground that finally became magnificent slopes and ridges and plateaus thousands of feet above their heads. They had come to the eastern paw of that giant animal of mountain ranges, the Andes; their route led directly up to the shoulders and then down its long spine to Peru.

They engaged Indian guides and had their belongings strapped to the backs of tough little mules. Upward they hiked, always upward, along a rough trail that led them between narrow breaks in the rocks and along twisting ridges and toward forests of laurels and conifers. The air thinned, plaguing Aimé with headaches and nausea.

Alexander, on the other hand, was filled with exhilaration by the ascent. Whenever he stopped and looked about, he sighed like a happy child at the wonderful pattern of life that nature was spreading before his eyes. Far below, shimmering in a heat haze, was the kingdom of the tropics—the forests of palms, the groves of banana and cacao trees, the long fields of cane sugar. That kingdom advanced only a short distance up the slopes, giving way quickly to the cotton and coffee plantations which, in their turn, surrendered the higher land to nut and rubber trees and the forests of conifers through which the trail was beginning to run. And far above the explorer, far above the crowns of the conifers, were the wind-swept plateaus where cattle grazed and Indian maize and potatoes and barley were cultivated. And finally, seeming to touch the sky and forever losing themselves in the clouds, were the peaks, snow-covered and sprinkled with Alpine grasses and herbs.

Alexander breathed deeply. Of all the spectacles he had come to South America to view, this was the one he had most wanted to see. Here, in these mountains, he had indeed found the harmony in nature.

The harmony in nature.

How those words carried him back over the years to that night so long ago on the Rhine River when, as a student vacationing from Göttingen, he had formed his grand theory of the interrelation of all natural objects. In his mind he heard again the very words he had spoken to Van Geuns by the campfire that night:

"Plants and rocks are related to their soil, their climate, their altitude. What else can account for the fact that one kind of plant will flourish and another die in exactly the same spot? All natural objects must be studied in their relationship to each other."

Then his mind focused on the letter he had written his friend on the eve of his departure for the New World. The words of that letter were so strong in his memory that they seemed to be speaking aloud:

"I shall endeavor to find out how nature's forces act upon one another, and in what manner the geographic environment exerts its influence on animals and plants. *In short, I must find out about the harmony in nature.*"

And now he was seeing that harmony in all its grandeur. Here, no longer hemmed in by the jungles of the Orinoco, he was witness to the influence of altitude on the growth of vegetation; he was seeing altitude hold out a restraining hand, refusing to allow certain plants to grow beyond a certain height and permitting other plants to take their place at that point.

His theory of the interrelation of all natural objects was no longer a theory in his mind. These mountains—as had Tenerife on a much smaller scale—were showing him that it was fact.

He began to walk again, swiftly, eager to be on his way. He must make notes of all he saw of the harmony in these mountains. He must record the temperature of the air all along the route to Peru. He must ask about the amount of annual rainfall at every town reached. He must continue his magnetic observations. Out of such work something grand would emerge. Exactly what that something would be, he did not know. But his every instinct told him it would be of lasting value to science.

Long days later the travelers came out on a vast plain. They saw the Indians grin and begin to jostle each other happily. The city of Sante Fé de Bogotá was straight ahead. At Bogotá there would be rest and dancing and drinking for the Indians. And grand dinners at the homes of the wealthy Spanish for the two fine gentlemen from across the sea. It was a magnificent city, the Indians said again and again. Beautiful and full of laughter.

Alexander and Aimé had heard of its magnificence before. In places as far away as Havana and Cuba, they had heard of its sprawling, ornate churches and monasteries, its vine-covered homes with their lavish inner gardens, and its surrounding lands where livestock grazed and a wide variety of crops were raised. They had also heard of its most distinguished citizen, Dr. José Celestino Mutis, and the knowledge that they would soon meet him dwarfed in their minds all the other wonders of the city.

Doctor. Botanist. Priest. Teacher. Metallurgist. Director of the Expedición Botánica. He was all these things, this Dr. Mutis. The explorers remained in Bogotá all through the summer of 1801 and came to know him well and to understand fully why his name was known to scientific circles all across Europe. The amount of work he had accomplished in his lifetime was staggering. He had gathered 20,000 plants in his herbarium. He had kept thirty artists busy for fifteen years painting the flowers and plants of the New World; he had on hand more than 2,000 examples of such paintings. He had sent plant collections to various European cities. Here was a man who had spoken with real eloquence to the Old World of the wonders found west of the Atlantic. To try to do half as much for South America as this tall, craggy-browed, and rather fearsome-looking priest had done, Alexander thought, was a goal worth trying for.

The explorers left Bogotá in September. Bound now for Quito in Ecuador, they passed through a mountain fairyland of balsam, palms, ferns, bamboo, and flowers. The flowers formed a dazzling, endless parade. Fuchsias and orchids clustered about the base of the trees and hid the lip of the trail from view.

But the fairyland soon gave way to an Andean nightmare. The explorers found themselves on narrow trails with yawning chasms to either side. Winds lashed them with such ferocity that they had to cling to the mules to keep from being hurled to their death on boulders hundreds of feet below. Rain drenched them. Hail, the size of large stones, drove them to the shelter of overhanging rocks. The rough ground tore their boots to shreds. Sharp stones slit the skin of their feet and little splashes of blood settled in the dust of the trail.

The wearing journey finally broke Alexander's temper. It happened when a group of stooped Indians appeared on the trail above the little village of Cartago. They were tiny people, each carrying the branch of a tree as if it were a walking stick. The leader of the group hailed Alexander and spoke a few words to him in very crude Spanish. The explorer's brows arched with surprise. He turned to one of his guides.

"This man wants to carry me down to the town."

The Indian guide nodded, finding this news not in the least astonishing. "That is right, Señor. He is a *caballito.*"

Alexander echoed the word. "*Caballito?* Little horse?"

"They all are, Señor. It has been that way for years, ever since the Spanish came. They are saddled by the Spaniards and are made to carry them over these hills. They lean on those sticks to hold up their riders. They are much better than mules."

Alexander's expression slowly changed as the guide spoke. His brows flattened and then came down over the bridge of his nose in a V of anger. His lips stretched into a thin, hard line.

"Saddles? Mules? You talk of them as you would talk of animals. Are they no better than animals?"

"In the eyes of the Spanish, no."

The blood was hot and furious in the explorer's face. He took a wrenching step away from the Indians. He couldn't stand to look at them another minute. To him, they were a bent, haggard symbol of the slavery that blackened the entire face of South America. How could one group of people so forget the human dignity of another group as to reduce them to beasts of burden? He pulled himself to a halt and faced the guide in cold fury. "Tell them to go away! Tell them they have met one white man who will not use a human being for a horse! I prefer to walk."

And walk he did, all the way across the Cauca Valley, pausing at Puracé volcano to study the physical and chemical properties of its gases before moving up into the rocky passes that twisted south to the Ecuadorian border.

The rainy season caught the travelers in those passes. The rain turned to sleet and snow as they struck higher altitudes. Their ragged clothing formed no protection against the weather. Their food ran low and what was left of it was soggy and indigestible. They spent the nights shivering in damp, shredding blankets, and the days gagging on volcanic fumes drifting across the trail.

Yet, in the face of these discomforts, the study of the harmony in nature continued. Plants were gathered, temperatures recorded, rainfall data collected, and geological formations investigated.

The explorers came out of the cold and crossed the border of Ecuador a few days after Christmas. They limped past the villages of Tuqueres and Ibarra. On January 6, 1802, almost eleven months to the day since their departure from Cuba, they entered the streets of Quito, once a center of the Inca civilization, and now a colonial city of earthquakes, luxury, and gaiety. There, for Alexander, disappointment turned into triumph.

As is so often the case with disappointment, Alexander's came unexpectedly.

It came one afternoon as he was showing his notebook to Carlos Montúfar, the youngest son of his host at Quito, Juan Pio Montúfar, Marqués de Selva Alegre. Carlos was tall, slender, of a dark complexion and an intense nature. Early in his stay at Quito, Alexander had recognized Carlos as being cut from the same mould as Aimé and himself. This young Spaniard, in his early twenties, was not interested in the social life of the city; he was as bored as the explorers with the round of dinners given in their honor; his eyes, like theirs, came alive only when the last glass of port had been consumed and he followed them out onto the terrace for the evening's study of the stars. Within a week, he had become Alexander and Aimé's constant companion on their geologic and botanical tours of the surrounding countryside.

He was eager for travel, eager to know the world beyond the limits of Quito and the Andes. Alexander thought wryly as he thumbed through his notebook with the young man: he finds his homeland commonplace and would think my country exciting, just as I find my homeland commonplace and think his country exotic.

That afternoon of the disappointment Alexander was keeping a promise made on his first night in Quito to Carlos. He was retracing for the young man's benefit his journey down from Cartagena. Before them on torn and stained pieces of paper was the record of ten months of hardship. It was also a very sharply drawn word portrait of the Andes mountains.

Alexander was speaking of the *caballitos* when Aimé entered the room, a letter in hand. "Come, sit down," Alexander called. "Carlos finds it hard to believe that—" His voice broke off. He frowned. There was an expression on Aimé's face that bewildered and somehow frightened him a little.

Aimé crossed the room stiffly, angrily.

"What is it?" Alexander asked. "What's wrong?"

Aimé held out the sheets of the letter. His big hand was closed tightly over them, crumpling them. "It is from my brother in France. I wrote him before we left Cuba that we were on our way to meet Baudin. I gave him a list of the towns at which we would be stopping. This reached the Post Office today." He thrust the letter into Alexander's hands and pointed to a paragraph near the bottom of the crumpled first page. "Read that!"

Alexander's voice was halting as he worked his way across the scrawled lines. "You will be interested to know—if you have not learned so already—that news has reached France that Captain Charles Baudin will not touch the Peruvian coast." Alexander stiffened, then read the sentence again. He glanced up at Aimé.

The Frenchman's face was blank with bitterness. "Read on."

"The newspapers say that Baudin has sent word home that he has changed his plans and is taking the eastern route round Africa to the East Indies. . . ."

Anger and disappointment flooded the explorer. He threw the letter down atop his open notebook on the table at which he and Carlos sat. He leaned forward and locked his hands together and began striking the table slowly and deliberately with them.

"Ten months of travel—and all for nothing." The words came out softly, almost in a whisper. He wanted to shout them aloud and forcibly had to hold his voice down. It wasn't fair! They had changed all their plans in the hope of meeting Baudin. They had known they were taking a gamble, but they had never considered it a losing gamble. They had been certain they would find the Captain in Peru. Now it turned out that they had done nothing but bungle their chance of seeing the United States.

He heard Aimé echoing his feelings. "We turned our backs on Canada. On Mexico. On Panama. What fools we've been! What utter fools!"

Aimé's hand crossed Alexander's line of vision, grabbed the letter and yanked it out of sight. Alexander felt rather than saw the Frenchman crumple it into a tight ball and fling it across the room. He heard it skip over the stone floor. But he did not lift his face. The letter had been covering the open notebook and now the explorer found himself staring at its soiled pages. He gazed at them without really seeing them. They were something just to be looked at while Aimé talked.

"It's all so stupid! We could be in the United States right now! We could be sailing down the Mississippi—"

Carlos said, "But I'm glad you've come here. Surely your whole trip hasn't been a waste."

Aimé replied, but Alexander did not hear what he said, for now he was really seeing the words in front of him. They acted like a tonic on him, clearing his brain and swiftly setting the disappointment to flight. How could anyone seriously harbor disappointment when he beheld these writings, he asked himself. Of course he had wanted to sail around the world with Captain Baudin, but he had lost sight of one vital fact in the past minutes—the fact that he had already seen a world. A very special world. It was one he would have missed had not he traveled through the Andes. It was the world of the harmony in nature.

His hand came away from the table and signaled Carlos and Aimé to silence. He lifted a face no longer hard to the young Spaniard.

"You're very right, Carlos. Our trip here was not a waste of time." He came to his feet and extended the notebook to Aimé. "We've studied the harmony in nature as never before. Now let's not *really* waste time by fretting. Let's get to work and see what those studies have to show us."

Aimé grinned with a suddenness surprising only to those unacquainted with his French ability to exchange effortlessly one mood for another. "Good! We gambled with Baudin, you and I, and we lost. And that is that."

"Yes, we gambled with Baudin," Alexander admitted. His gaze dropped to the notebook in Aimé's big hands. "But, somehow, I don't think we've lost."

No longer in a hurry to reach Lima, he remained at Quito for six months, dividing his time between excursions through the surrounding countryside and long sessions at his notebook.

He studied and then studied again all the words written since Cartagena. He pored over the figures he had collected on the temperature, wind velocity, and annual rainfall at various levels in the Andes. Slowly two startling facts began to show through the words and figures. He remembered his feeling on the trail above Hondo: that something wonderful would result from his journey down to Quito. He knew he was beginning to see that something.

The first fact concerned the vegetation of the Andes. His notes had shown him that all the plants extending up the slopes could be grouped into six definite zones. To see these zones more clearly, he sketched the profile of a mountain on a blank page in his notebook. It was a simple sketch, no more than a large inverted V. He then assigned his six zones to the eastern slope.

He sat back and regarded his work.

So far so good.

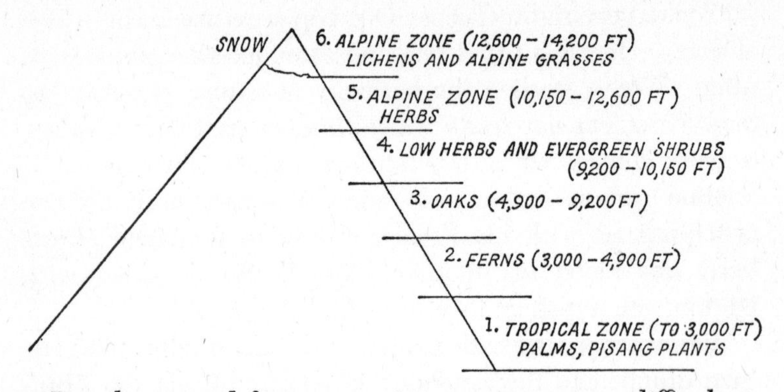

But the second fact was going to prove more difficult to digest.

At that moment, Aimé entered the room and, coming to stand at his shoulder, gazed down at the drawing. The Frenchman understood immediately what his friend had done.

"Alex! It's wonderful," he cried. "All that plant life compressed into six zones. It makes the complexity of nature so simple. Now anyone will be able to see how altitude influences vegetation."

Instantly, Alexander was shaking his head. In his final sentence, Aimé had struck at the heart of the second fact. "You've missed a step, Aimé. The ascending altitude is creating various climates up the side of the mountains. And those various climates are responsible for the changes in plant life."

"Various climates?" Aimé echoed. "All on one mountainside?"

"Yes. And all the factors of climate—wind, sun, rainfall, temperature—they are the things responsible for the six zones. Listen. Why do tropical plants grow only at the base of the mountain? Because the heat is collected down there. And why are Alpine grasses found only at the summit? Because up there it is always winter. And why is one side of a mountain rich with vegetation and the other so often barren? Because the rain clouds cannot get over the peaks to wet them. Even the soil is conditioned by climate; for example, it can be carried downhill from one place to another by the rain water." He touched the drawing; the touch was almost a caress. "You can understand what I have here, can't you? It's a picture of climate and vegetation working in harmony."

Aimé met his friend's enthusiasm with doubt. "It's an interesting theory, Alex. But will the world accept it? It's very difficult to realize that climate can change so drastically and exert so much influence in such a small area on the face of the earth as a mountain."

Alexander nodded. Uncomfortably. What the botanist said was true. Some method was needed to take his second fact out of the realm of pure theory and turn it into useful fact. But what sort of a method?

Quite suddenly, a third fact fell across his mind, a fact already accepted by the world about the relationship between climate and earth—the zones of life. They stretched northward from the equator to the north pole. He began to sketch them in his notebook, placing them in the blank space directly below his mountain. He was after something. Exactly what, he did not know. He only knew that it was obvious to everyone that these broad zones of life were influenced by climate.

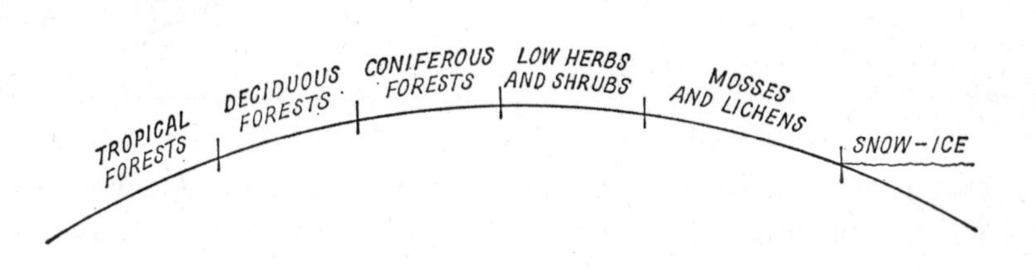

After he had finished, he pondered his drawings, one above the other, for a long while.

Strange, he thought.

There are six zones on the mountain.

And six zones of life stretching north from the equator.

Strange—

Then what he was seeing was no longer merely strange. It was downright staggering. He gasped, suddenly aware that he had stumbled upon a greater harmony than he had ever hoped to find.

The zones of the mountain and the zones of life *coincided.*

He brought his face down close to the page.

Surely he had made some error.

But there was no error.

The zones—all of them—coincided.

He flipped the page over and began to draw swiftly on a fresh sheet. He placed his mountain on the curve of the earth and then he drew a series of lines from mountain to earth.

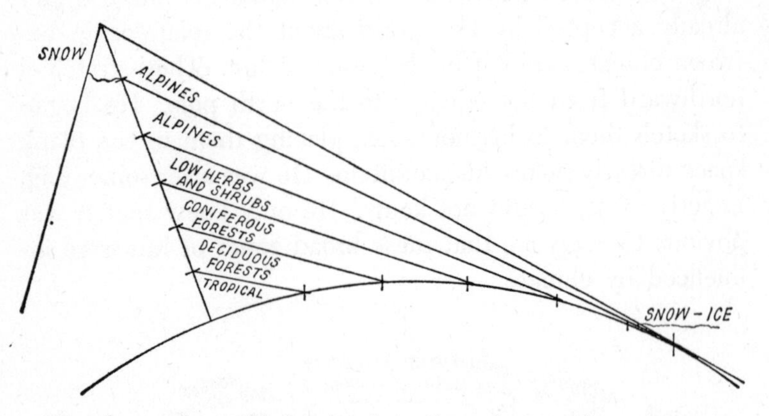

He thrust himself far back in his chair. His eyes were glittering. His voice was sharp with the thrill of discovery and the pride of having proved his theory correct. "Look,

Aimé! The zones on the mountain are the same as the zones of life. We already know that those broad zones on earth are influenced—made what they are—by climate. Now, by comparing them with the ones on the mountain, we have proof of how the vegetation on the mountain is influenced by climate. It's as simple as that! And because we are dealing with a small area, we can see how every plant on the mountain is affected by climate."

In the years that followed, the relationship of climate and soil and vegetation was to become so basic to man's knowledge that it would be taken for granted. But, at this moment, in this year of 1802, it was a startling discovery, a fresh concept of the physical world. For the first time in history, man was beginning to see the dependence of plants on climate and soil conditions.

Alexander would spend years bringing his infant concept to adulthood. He would nurture it daily with facts gathered from over the face of the globe. And one day, in its maturity, it would father new fields for botanical studies. The horizons of atmospheric studies would widen because of it. And the economy of agriculture would profit from it. Farmers the world over would come to understand maximum rainfall, seasonal frosts, and dew point as prime tools of their calling. And geographers would come to understand that natural phenomena cannot be studied independently; they must be studied in their relationships to one another before the wonders of the earth can be fully recognized. These understandings first stirred that afternoon in Quito in the hands of Alexander von Humboldt.

One of his finest hours had struck.

But it was to be followed swiftly by another—and, in Alexander's mind, a finer—hour of triumph.

After he had closed his notebook that afternoon, he

walked to an upper window in the Montúfar house. He gazed thoughtfully southward. One hundred miles down from Quito lay a mountain called Chimborazo.

Chimborazo.

To think of it as a mere mountain was to do it a grave injustice. It was a fabulous, heaven-touching tower of granite and snow. Reaching an estimated height of over 20,000 feet, it was the highest known peak in the New World.

As he gazed southward, a dream, an ambition, was forming in the explorer's mind. He had traveled through jungles to establish the point of connection between the two great rivers of South America. He had determined astronomically the geographical locations of well over one hundred spots. With Aimé, he had collected thousands of plants and had journeyed through the Andes to find his cherished harmony in nature. Now his dream was to stand on the summit of Chimborazo, at an altitude never before attained by man.

CHAPTER TEN

The Heights of Chimborazo

ALEXANDER DID NOT know exactly when he decided to climb Chimborazo.

He knew only that the mountain had held a peculiar fascination for him from the day he had first sighted its peak hazy in a mist shredding in the morning sun. That fascination had grown little by little all during his stay at Quito. He could not pass a window in the southern wall of the Montúfar home without pausing to contemplate its slopes mottled with whites and grays and greens; at night he found his gaze repeatedly descending from the stars and trying to pierce the darkness in vain attempts to determine its outline, and sometimes he imagined he could discern its great bulk glimmering dully and coldly in the moonlight.

His decision to climb Chimborazo was without real scientific basis. He could tell himself that he wanted a commanding view of the harmony in nature on surrounding mountains, but he had only to look at the peak to know that it was almost always shrouded in a creamy mist that made a mockery of such a hope. He could tell himself that he wanted to climb higher than any man before him and that he wanted to study the changing vegetation on the slopes. Both were true. But neither went far enough. The truth of the matter was that his decision came from sources thoroughly human and mysterious, and beyond plausible explanation. It was founded in an emotion experienced—but only vaguely understood—by man since the beginning of time when faced with the overpowering and the seemingly unconquerable. It was an emotion perhaps best expressed in later years by the adventurer who said, "Why do I climb a mountain? Because it is there." The mountain—any mountain—was and always would be a challenge to a certain breed of men. Alexander was of that breed.

But he was not actually aware of his decision to challenge Chimborazo until he heard himself putting that challenge into words for Aimé in a conversation that, until then, had centered on matters of an entirely different nature. He was not a little surprised at how naturally the subject of climbing the mountain had entered their talk.

Then, when he saw Aimé smile and heard him say, "I've been wondering when you'd finally get around to *that,*" he was no longer surprised. He realized that the desire to attempt the peak had been in mind for days, blossoming slowly in the fertile soil of the fascination. Aimé had seen in him what he himself had missed: that there was no other direction in which the fascination could logically move.

He replied to Aimé's knowing smile with, "Well, what do you think of the idea? It's possible for us—you and I, my friend—to stand on the highest point on earth ever reached by man."

Aimé's answer was prompt and a succinct commentary on their working relationship. "Wherever you go I go." It was as simple as that.

Until that moment, Carlos Montúfar had hovered on the perimeter of the conversation. Now he stepped forward eagerly to plead to be taken with them. He had lived in the shadow of Chimborazo all his life. He, too, had felt its magnetism. He could not possibly remain at the gates of the Montúfar home and watch his two new friends march southward to their appointment with Chimborazo. He could not spend a day merely twiddling his thumbs while they struggled up those snowy slopes. He had to go with them.

"And you shall. Agreed, Aimé?"

"Agreed."

And so, quickly and effortlessly, it was settled. Chimborazo would be attacked. And, with luck, defeated.

But you do not decide to climb a mountain and then merely walk up its side. You plan a route. You plan your supplies. You decide on your gear and clothes. And then you practice. And practice. And then practice some more.

The volcano of Pichincha was their rehearsal ground. They tried for its summit on April 14, failing because of giddiness due to the thin air, and then again on May 26, when they made their way to a height of 14,940 feet.

They were ready for Chimborazo on June 9, 1802. They rode south out of Quito and down past the cities of Latacunga and Ambato and, on June 22nd, reined up at the base of Chimborazo. Alexander, running his eyes up over the craggy face of the mountain to its crown of frozen white, noted the date with interest. It seemed an omen of good things to come. Three years ago this very day he and Aimé had struggled, panting and bleeding, up the walls of Tenerife. They had won their fight with that mountain. Perhaps they would win another tomorrow.

But he wondered. Tenerife was a dwarf compared with this silent hulk. Chimborazo, looming so far above that it gave the impression of leaning out over you, had a look of hard anger to it. No, it wasn't anger. It was scorn.

They slept the night away in the village and, with four guides, got under way before daybreak of the 23rd. Anyone watching them would have thought they were out for a morning stroll. They walked at an easy pace that looked rather careless. Actually their pace was steady; the look of carelessness came from a deliberate effort not to tire themselves too quickly. They merely had to glance at the steepening slopes above them to sense the exhaustion that lay ahead.

Slowly through the break of dawn and through the hours that followed it, the mountain dropped away behind them. The first 6,000 feet, Alexander later recalled, were quite easy, gradual and sloping. But, before they had crossed the 7,000 foot level, they knew Chimborazo had cast aside its good humor. The ground sloped sharply, as if wishing it could thrust itself outward and become vertical to the plains below. Giant rocks appeared in the path of the climbers. They had to be worked round or climbed over.

The air joined the mountain in toying with these little creatures who had the audacity to think they could win a battle fought against nature. It turned bitter cold, purpled their flesh, and made blocks of ice of their lungs. It sucked away its oxygen and left it on the lower slopes so that by the time they reached the snow line they were panting with every step and showing little or no enthusiasm over the butterfly Aimé captured at such a height.

At 15,000 feet the mountain and the air won their first victory of the day. The native guides from Calpi halted, ankle deep in snow, and faced their employer. Their brown faces had a bluish tinge to them. They had been talking among themselves for the past half-hour and now they pushed one of their number—their senior by age—toward

Alexander. The explorer felt himself stiffen. It was not hard to guess what was coming. Though they had lived their lives in the shadow of Chimborazo, they were not accustomed to the discomforts found at this altitude.

The Indian who faced him was a simple, leathery-faced man without the ability to explain gently the decision of his companions. And so he substituted action for words. He loosened the straps of his pack and let the thing fall to the ground. Snow puffed out from under it. The Indian shrugged; his words seemed unnecessarily harsh in the still, bitter air.

"We are going back. If you are wise you will follow us. God did not mean this mountain to be climbed."

He started to move downhill past Alexander before he had stopped talking. His companions, dropping their packs, fell into step behind him.

Though he had been ready for the words, he was totally unprepared for the sudden movement of the Indians, having anticipated that the crisis would pass after several minutes of argument and the agreement to raise their wages. He spun after them, caught up with the leader, and faced him about.

He was later unable to recall exactly what he said to the man. He remembered that he had pleaded with him and that Carlos had appeared from somewhere behind Aimé and had shouted angrily, "I'll have you whipped for this! I order you to stay!"

It was a typical Spanish threat, thoroughly useless. The Indians merely sniffed and replied that they would gladly risk a whipping rather than death in the cold. The leader shrugged himself free of Alexander and, motioning his companions to follow him, turned his back on the summit. Aimé and Carlos moved close to Alexander to watch the brown figures diminish in the distance until they were no more than tiny sticks far below them. The air was very still and very thin, and from time to time they could hear one of the Indians shout the advice to turn back before it was too late. Finally, they could hear the shouts no more.

There was only one thing for the climbers to do after the guides had departed, and that was to sling the abandoned packs to their shoulders and get on their way again. They walked slowly now over the steep ground, testing their every step in the crusted snow. They were bent far forward; somehow that position made breathing easier. Occasionally they looked up and when they did they saw a gray mist curling in on them from the left. When it closed over them, it not only hid the summit from view but all the rocky ground circling them beyond a distance of five yards.

They came out of the mist a short time later and found themselves on a narrow ridge of snow no more than eight to ten inches wide. To either side were chasms designed to freeze a man with fright. To the right was a snowy wall falling away to a narrow ravine 1,000 feet below; and to the left snow clung to an almost vertical slope of rock. Where it ended the travelers could not determine, for the mist had gathered in it to curl smokily and sleepily.

The explorers came off the ridge to behold a jumble of rock rising almost vertically into another layer of fog. In the next hour, Alexander was reminded more than once of the lava cone atop Tenerife. It required hands and feet and all their will power to worm their way to the crest of that pile of rock. Every handhold had to be checked before use, a wise precaution as, more often than not, the rock dissolved in their hands and, bursting, rained down in a shower of jagged chips on their faces and shoulders. And when it did not burst it cut long and deep into hands that no longer had any feeling in the fingers, but only lumps of dull pain out under the fingernails.

In the mist above the rocks they located another narrow ridge of snow. The mist was so thick that they could barely make out the creamy explosions of their own breath. Alexander beckoned Aimé to his side to check with him the tube barometer he had struggled out of his pack. Aimé's face was blue-gray as he balanced himself there on that narrow ledge with nothingness inches away from his feet. He gasped, not with his mouth hanging agape, but with his lips stretched and pulled back and his teeth clamped hard together. He was as much like a snarling beast as a man. Behind them Carlos stood swaying and half buckling at the knees. From time to time, he shook his head as if trying to clear his mind after being struck a tremendous blow. One eye was a flaming red where a blood vessel had burst.

Alexander's lacerated hands left smears of blackened blood on the tube barometer as he opened it. It showed them that they had achieved a height of 17,300 feet, little more than 2,000 feet above the height they had reached on their second Pichincha climb.

"How far?" Aimé gasped, flicking his eyes toward the summit out of sight in the gray mist.

Alexander was a moment in replying. He was trying to get the barometer back in his pack and his fingers were not working properly. His expression was hard with the lumps of pain out under his nails. "Another 6,000 feet at least."

Aimé swallowed, making a popping sound deep in his throat. "Well, let's get at it."

The next part of the climb proved to be the hardest and most dangerous part of the ordeal. One by one, crawling up over jagged rocks and stumbling along twisting ridges, they fell victim to the thin air. The first signs of danger were the increasing attacks of light headedness, followed swiftly by a giddiness that left each climber with the odd feeling that he was standing still while the mountain was beginning to swing underfoot. Then came nausea. Alexander bent far over, retching. When he straightened and passed a hand across his mouth, blood came away on his knuckles, showing him that his lips—or, from the sour-sweet taste on his tongue, his gums—had started to split. He was not particularly alarmed. He had become well acquainted with these discomforts of altitude on his previous climbs. Once on Pichincha he had been flung to his hands and knees by a violent stomach cramp that had knifed up through the dizziness.

He turned to watch his companions clambering up behind him. Aimé walked at a half stumble, catching himself on one hand whenever he fell, and dragging Carlos along with the other. The Frenchman was deathly pale and the blood clotting on his lips stood out like a splash of crimson paint on a white canvas. He staggered from side to side as if buffeted by a fierce wind, though the air on the mountainside was dead, unmoving. But Carlos was the truly frightening one to see. The eye with the burst blood vessel glowed like a burning coal, giving him the look of a madman. His breath was screaming like a saw trying to cut through steel; red bubbled thickishly in his nostrils and at the corners of his mouth with every breath, and there was a blackish thread coming out of one ear and trailing down over the lobe. Alexander caught the young Spaniard when he came within arm's reach and held him up straight.

Carlos shook himself free, proudly and angrily. "Leave me alone! I'm all right."

Alexander peered at him closely. The collar of the Spaniard's jacket was open and the muscles in his neck were working violently. Alexander asked, pointlessly, "Are you sure?"

The madman eye burned into his face with red humor for a moment. Then it winked. "Never better."

Aimé began to laugh. It came from deep inside him, but it managed to sound dry and fleshless. "I just remembered Thomas Appleton."

"Appleton?"

"The English gardener. Back on Tenerife."

"What about him?"

"I just remembered what he said after we'd crossed the Retama: 'It wasn't exactly a stroll through the park, was it?' That's what he said. Right down to the last word. Remember? Oh, if he only knew!"

And then they were all laughing and thinking that Appleton was the most humorous man in the world and that they had gone a little crazy up here in the thin air. Alexander didn't mind because, laughing, there was something indomitable about his two friends. Let them bleed from the mouth and ears. Let the cold burn their lungs and throats raw. At this moment, they were men to whom the mountain could do no harm, even if they were sentenced to scale its sides through all eternity.

When they had calmed themselves, he said, "We're fools to stand here wasting our strength. If this fog would only clear. We must be close to the end, though."

They were close to the end, as they learned in another half-hour, but not the end as Alexander meant it. The mist suddenly dissolved—the explorer attributed its abrupt disappearance to electricity in the air—as they were well along a wide ridge, and the summit of Chimborazo thrust itself into view. The whiteness of its slopes glittered against a sky that was both pale and blinding at the same time. In the thin, clear air the peak seemed so close that, for a moment, they were fooled into believing that they only had to stretch out their arms to touch it. They came together silently, hardly breathing, to view as a unit that icy dome. It was a movement prompted by the odd combination of fierce pride and terrible loneliness: the shared pride of having come this far above the haunts of mankind, and the hollow, humbling loneliness that man always feels when he stands where no other man has walked.

As swiftly and as silently as they had come together, the climbers separated and fell into line for the final attack on the summit. It was as if they were now controlled by one mind. No one set the pace. They all moved with equal impatience, their eyes fastened on the peak and squinted against the stark yellowness of the icy disk above and behind it that was the sun. They even breathed in unison. And their brains, refreshed now that victory was at hand, simultaneously performed the same mathematical calculation: it could not be more than another 2,000 feet to the top. Just another 2,000 feet. Perhaps less.

Alexander was in the lead and he was moving so swiftly that later he swore he had been running. Snow flew out from under his shoes. He could hear Aimé's soprano breath behind him. His spirit was singing and he was unconscious of all pain and all coldness. Because his eyes were on the peak he did not see until the last moment the danger fast approaching. Some little warning instinct caused him to lower them to the ground in front of him for just a moment. That was all he needed.

He pulled himself up suddenly, flinging his arms wide to halt the plunging Aimé. Bonpland crashed into his arm, his momentum carrying him another step forward before he could halt himself.

"What's the matter—"

His voice broke. Carlos came up to his side, started to ask the same question, and then fell bitterly silent.

German, Frenchman, and Spaniard stared at the end of their journey.

It was not the sort of ending Alexander had envisioned earlier down in the mist. It was one he could hardly accept at this moment. But it was the end. And there was no argument about it. They would go no further.

They had come to a stop at the edge of a monstrous gash that nature had carved in the forehead of Chimborazo. The gash, a long ravine curving away out of sight around the side of the mountain, was, they gauged, sixty feet across and four hundred feet deep. Alexander could see that the ridge on which they now stood began again on the far side of the gaping wound, but he could also see that there was no way across to that other ridge. Disappointment was sour wine against his tongue. In these final moments of the battle, the mountain had won—after knowing all along that it would win. It would not experience this day the indignity of tiny human beings walking across its white crown.

But its victory was to prove a hollow one.

With great care, the climbers removed the barometer from Alexander's pack and opened it. Down on their hands and knees, they peered at it and found that it stood at thirteen inches, eleven and two-tenths lines. According to the barometric formula given by Laplace, they had reached a height of 19,286 feet.

They had come higher up the face of the earth than any other man in history.

They had established an altitude record that would stand unchallenged in the annals of mountain climbing for another quarter of a century.

They had proved that man had the stamina and the bodily equipment to reach the top of the world, thereby laying the first stone in the roadway that would lead to the exploration of all the world's highest summits. The final stone in that roadway would be set down close to a century and a half later by Edmund Hillary on Mount Everest.

Alexander sat down on a patch of dry ground, deliberately putting his back to the peak. No matter that he had not reached the top of that peak. No matter that he had never felt so cut off from the realm of man in all his life. No matter that he ached from head to foot and that his boots were sodden with snow turned to water.

He had done what no other mortal had done since the beginning of time.

He knew that the world would find his other contributions to science and geography more practical and valuable, but he also knew that he would cherish the memory of this day, this very moment, to the end of his life. In his own mind, this was his greatest triumph.

CHAPTER ELEVEN

The Palace of Underground Fantasy

IN JULY OF 1802 the work at Quito was finished. It was time to move on.

At daybreak, Alexander shook hands with his host of the past weeks, the Marqués, and for the last time saw the magnificent gate of the Montúfar home swing shut. When he glanced over his shoulder at noontime he found that the jagged horizon now concealed the equator city of earthquakes and luxury from view. Where the spires of Quito had been only a few minutes ago, there was now a stretch of blinding azure sky.

Six mules formed a staggered column behind the explorer. They ambled along quite unconcernedly beneath the boxes of luggage, scientific gear, food, and plant collections strapped to their backs. Whenever the whips of the two Indian drivers bit into their flanks, they limited a show of their emotions to slight and arrogant flicks of their long ears. Little clouds of dust came up from under their hoofs. They swished their tails lazily at flies and purposefully at the drivers.

At Alexander's side was Aimé, walking with the arm-swinging, rolling gait that had remained with him since his days as a naval surgeon. The Frenchman was whistling softly a martial air that Alexander could not identify and, just beyond him, Carlos was stepping out in unconscious rhythm with it, as proud and erect as a conquistador. The young Spaniard's eyes were bright with excitement. Now and again, he threw back his head and breathed deeply, as if he had spent his entire life indoors. He wore an outfit of sturdy wool, especially purchased for the journey; the cloth had the shine and thickness of newness to it; not a patch, not a worn thread showed. Alexander smiled. The raw recruit appearance of the costume would diminish as the hours merged into days, the days into weeks. Slowly it would acquire that tough, sweat-white look of the trail veteran.

As he walked, hearing the curses of the drivers and the uncaring snorts of the mules in reply, Alexander wondered idly why he had permitted Carlos to share the remainder of his New World adventures. The expedition, already heavily weighted down with equipment, really had no room for another man and his luggage, particularly one who, neither scientist nor practiced explorer, could not hope to make a real contribution to the work. Perhaps, the explorer thought, I agreed to his company in the face of parental protests—and heated protests they had been, for the Spanish do not relinquish their young easily—because I saw in him the same painful yearnings I saw in myself years ago. It was more likely that the Chimborazo climb had welded a blood-tie between young Montúfar and the expedition; after all, you don't walk with a man to an impossible height and then bid him farewell.

Whatever the reasons behind it, Alexander at a future date would find consolation in his decision. He would recall what he could not possibly know now—that on this July day in 1802 Carlos had a little less than eight years of life left him. Upon his return to Ecuador, he would give himself up to the flames of revolution beginning to crackle throughout South America and would join an uprising against the government of his homeland. In 1810, the body that was so lithe and eager would crumple in the dust a split second after seven rifles had bucked in the hands of a Spanish firing squad; and from that body would be torn a heart to be burned in the plaza in Quito. Alexander would reflect that at least he had given the young man his chance at happiness before death in its ugliest form sought him out.

The travelers, pausing a day en route to climb the volcano of Cotopaxi, moved south past Chimborazo. Was it their imagination or did that mountain seem a bit sullen now that it had been nearly conquered by man? Their course was to carry them generally southeast to the Amazon Valley, then west across to Trujillo on the Pacific coast, and finally down to Lima. There, they would engage a ship for Mexico. After traversing Mexico, they would sail up to the United States. And then—Europe.

Alexander and Aimé had realized while at Quito that the time left them in South America was short. "We've been here almost three years," they told each other, "and the weather is beginning to get to our equipment. There's no use trying to carry on with equipment that's falling apart."

Then, too, the wealth of material they had collected must be put in order for presentation to the scientific world. And they had to admit, rather sheepishly, that they were getting a bit homesick; with increasing frequency, they found themselves wondering what scientific marvels Paris, Berlin, Rome, and Madrid had unearthed in their absence. And so they had set aside a welter of dreams—explorations of Panama, the Philippines, and the South Seas—and had decided on an itinerary that would untimately lead them back to the Old World, where they would put their findings in order and plot future adventures.

From Chimborazo they moved down a long valley to the town of Riobamba. There, quite unexpectedly, Alexander came upon the study that was to occupy a major share of the time remaining to him in the New World.

It was while at Riobamba that he heard of the aging Leandro Zapla who lived at nearby Likan. Zapla was an Indian prince who could trace his blood line back to the hazy days before the conquest of his homeland by the Inca hordes of Tapayupangi. He was also the owner of several manuscripts which the magistrate at Riobamba assured the explorer were of great historical interest and value.

Always curious, Alexander rode over to Likan one morning and reined up before a shack set down in the middle of a dirt yard filled with farm animals and half-naked children. His first glimpse of Zapla erased from mind the squalor of the setting. The appearance and demeanor of the Indian transformed his poor home into a palace. He was every inch a prince, his tall, lean frame erect, his voice soft and his Spanish impeccable, his manner polite and welcoming. He was a very old man, with gray-black hair falling to his shoulders, and with a face that was all angles and the color and texture of leather. His clothes were worn and faded, but spotless from countless washings. He bowed politely when Alexander, introducing himself, stated the purpose of his visit.

"But of course you shall see my manuscripts," he said, and beckoned the explorer into the dusk of the main room of the shack. A low platform ran round the walls and placed on it were straw mats for sleeping. There was a makeshift table at the center of the room. The air was cool, the heat of the day yet to come, and Zapla had a fire going in an open hearth. An Indian woman smiled at them from where she knelt at a large earthen bowl in front of the flames. The floor was merely dirt pounded hard by the passage of many feet. Somehow it became a surface of rich marble as Zapla crossed over it.

He led Alexander to an intricately carved chest in the corner and, kneeling before it to lift its lid, he said without rancor, "Not much has been left the Indian in this country. But I have managed to retain a few treasures. These are the most precious of the lot."

Set neatly in the chest, one atop the other, were the manuscripts. Judging from the worn, mellow look of their hide covers, they were of great age. When Zapla opened the topmost one, the pages revealed were yellow and crackled to the touch. Zapla moved calloused hands over those amber pages with the same gentleness with which he might stroke the forehead of a newborn babe. Had not Alexander been so taken with the strange, faded writing working its way neatly down the exposed sheets he would have seen a dreamy, faraway expression rise momentarily in his host's eyes.

But the creased face that Zapla turned to him seconds later was touched with a grave sort of humor. He said blandly, "I am very fortunate that the Spaniards think more of gold than they do of books. Otherwise, I should have lost these years ago." He began placing the manuscripts on the sleeping platform. "They have come down to me from my ancestors. They are in the Purugayan language and were written more than two centuries ago. Perhaps you would care not just to view them but read them?"

"I should care to very much," Alexander said. "But, unfortunately, I do not understand the Purugayan tongue."

Zapla removed the last of the manuscripts. Revealed now at the bottom of the chest was a sheaf of newer paper. "But, *fortunately*, a later ancestor had the foresight to make this translation of them into Spanish." He carried the bundle of newer papers to the table at the center of the room and beckoned Alexander to seat himself. "I think the translation will provide you with several hours of interesting reading."

Several hours of interesting reading—that was hardly an apt description of the time the fascinated explorer spent at the translation. Out of its pages flowed a story of a people rich in cultural achievements, rich in tradition and at the same time caught in a web of superstition. It was a story of agriculture, mathematics, astronomy—and natural disaster.

One tale in particular captured the fancy of this Humboldt who never tired of scaling volcanoes and peering into their steaming depths. He spoke of it to Aimé and Carlos that very night at dinner. It concerned the eruption of the volcano of Nevado de Altár, which had been known to the ancients as Capa-urku, "Chief of the Mountains."

"From what I can gather, it was taller than Chimborazo at the time. Its eruption lasted for seven years. Mind you, seven years! The ashes and smoke were so thick at Likan that there was no daylight in all that time!"

Aimé cocked a skeptical eyebrow. "Sounds a bit exaggerated, if you ask me."

"Not really," Carlos put in. "I have seen Quito blanketed with ashes from Cotopaxi for as many as eighteen hours."

"And consider the ground hereabouts," Alexander argued. "The thickness of the volcanic material which covers it testifies to a great eruption in bygone days. And look at the

Nevado de Altár today. It no longer compares in size with Chimborazo. It must have blown itself right apart."

He returned to the Zapla house daily for the remainder of the week, continuing his reading of the days before the Spaniards. He learned that the priests of the time had interpreted the eruption of their Capa-urku as an omen of a coming change in earth and life. "A new order of deities is coming," they had intoned, "by whom the gods we now worship will be driven away. Let us not withstand the decrees of fate."

As he read of this ancient civilization, Alexander was reminded of so many things he had seen and heard during his travels throughout South America: the crude drawings high on the rocks along the Orinoco; the story told by the venerable old Tamanac—how like Zapla he was!—of the fruits of the mauritia palm producing new people for the world after the "time of the great waters"; the stone at Bogotá, cut in the shape of a heptagon and used by the Indians long ago in the calculation of their calendars; the information that astronomers in the centuries before the Spanish conquest had been able to draw a meridian line and observe the actual movement of the solstice; the richness of the Carib language, a tongue capable of embracing abstract ideas such as eternity, the future, and existence.

He wanted to strike the table angrily there in Zapla's poor home when he thought of such things. The Spaniards with their silver helmets and their glittering lances and their snorting horses had assaulted these civilizations and had ground them under their heels and had sent word back to Europe that the natives of the New World were savages. And Europe had believed them and still believed them today, viewing the Indians as ignorant, godless, and superstitious. The fact of the matter was that the original peoples of the New World had built civilizations that would put to shame many a proud nation across the Atlantic if such nations ever bothered to lower their haughty noses and make a comparison.

Once Alexander's anger forced him outdoors for a breath of fresh air. He stood in Zapla's sagging doorway, breathing deeply and thinking that Europe was the ignorant one. It had never bothered to open its eyes to the true qualities of South America; it was so much simpler merely to grab at its gold and silver and cast its peoples aside as mere curiosities of a capricious God. Well, it was high time that Europe was jolted out of its lazy blindness. Alexander was certain he was the right man to make a proper job of that jolting. Stretching and feeling the keenness of the air in his lungs, he promised himself to get down in earnest finally to the work he had wanted to do all through his travels—the task of collecting data on the ancient civilizations of the New World that would make those lands across the Atlantic sit up and take notice.

The land south of Riobamba revealed itself to be a treasure house for such an undertaking. Moving toward the Amazon Valley, the expedition crossed over into Peru in August, 1802, bringing Alexander to the very heart of the world of the Inca, that fabulous tribe that believed it sprang from the loins of four brothers, all bearing the title *Ayar*, who had emerged at the beginning of time from a region called the "House of Dawn." Everywhere there was startling evidence of their once flourishing civilization, a civilization wantonly destroyed by Spanish troops thirsting after gold.

Along with descriptions of plant and geologic life there began to appear in Alexander's notebook and letters observations of ancient Inca accomplishments, such as:

"On the Paramo of Assuay, at a height of 15,000 feet, the magnificent road of the Incas may still be traced. This causeway reaches almost to Cuzco (a distance of several hundred miles) and is constructed entirely of hewn stone; it is perfectly straight and resembles the finest roads of the ancient Romans."

And:

"The Incas did not use wheeled conveyances. Consequently, long flights of steps were constructed at intervals, with resting-places, to overcome the steep slopes. When Pizarro and Almagro conquered Peru, they availed themselves of these military roads, and the Spanish cavalry found these steps formidable obstacles, especially in the early phase of the conquest, when the Spaniards made use of horses only."

In addition to the roads, he saw aqueducts, irrigation systems, and the sides of mountains cut into terraces for farming. His blood boiled at the sight of them. The Spanish had destroyed the roads by tearing out their rocks and quarrying them. They had allowed aqueducts and the irrigation systems to fall into ruin.

And how had the Incas reacted to their Spanish conquerors? How had they fought back? Of many examples collected of their opposition, one always sent a chill along Alexander's spine:

"I visited the extensive sulphur mines at Tiscan. The rebel Indians conceived the idea of setting fire to these sulphur works, after the earthquake of 1797; certainly the most horrible plan ever devised by a people driven to despair. They hoped by this means to produce an eruption by which the whole province of Alausi should be destroyed."

The explorer set aside temporarily his observations of the Incas upon reaching the Amazon Valley. The party moved along the turbulent Río de Cuancabamba to the upper Amazon, lingering there for seventeen days, gathering plants, surveying the lush countryside, and studying the remarkable healing properties of the bark of the chinchona tree.

It was while on the upper Amazon that Alexander's endless readings of the earth's magnetic intensity began to bear fruit. He discovered that he had now come far enough south of the equator to indicate the invisible line separating the terrestrial magnetic field of the Northern Hemisphere from that of the Southern Hemisphere. He fixed that invisible line, that magnetic equator, at 7° 27′ southern latitude and 81° 8′ western longitude.

Upon leaving the Amazon and climbing the Andes southwest toward Trujillo on the Pacific coast, he had reason to begin again his notes on the Inca world. Near Gualgayoc, he entered a mountain region rich in silver. Stopping at one mine, he watched Indians, huge baskets hanging down their backs by means of straps across their foreheads, carrying silver by the ton down from the mine entrance to a smelter. They inched their way along a narrow trail of slippery clay. Their eyes were squinted against the great weights they bore. They were as skinny as posts and the muscles in their shoulders stood out like bunched hemp. Perspiration ran off their faces as they set down their burdens at the smelter, burdens that had resulted in the flow of thirty-two millions piasters' worth of silver into the King of Spain's purse in the past thirty years. The workers did not rest between trips; they immediately hurried back up the trail; they walked bent far forward, as if their years as beasts of burden had cracked their spines.

Alexander's mouth thinned with rage. He had thought the miners of the Bayreuth and Fichtel mountains in difficult straits. Their state was as nothing in comparison with the harrowing circumstances to which this once proud race had been reduced.

The most heartbreaking example of the Inca state was

seen further southwest at the plateau city of Cajamarca, located some ninety miles inland from the Pacific coast. It was now a colonial city of wide thoroughfares meeting neatly at right angles, and of low clay buildings. It had once been the seat of empire of the Inca ruler, Atahualpa.

Atahualpa had been gone more than two hundred and fifty years from the South American scene. Francisco Pizarro and his Spanish legions had taken Cajamarca in 1532 and had made the mightly Atahualpa a prisoner in his own palace; the following year they had cut him down with their swords. After that, they had slowly and methodically destroyed his empire, draining it of its silver resources, slaughtering the most stubborn of his people, and turning the rest of them into farmers, servants, and carvers of silver.

Atahualpa's palace still loomed above the plain which stretched out from Cajamarca, falling to ruin, its magnificent columns chipped, its great courtyards silent and overgrown with weeds. Somewhere deep in that vast, decaying structure was the room in which Pizarro had held Atahualpa prisoner. There was a mark high on one of its walls. It indicated the height to which the Inca had promised his Spanish captor he would fill the room with gold in trade for his freedom.

Alexander, naturally, was eager to see the palace. Upon being introduced to several of Atahualpa's descendants yet living at Cajamarca, he stated his wish and heard one of them reply, "I shall be happy to take you there, Excellency."

The speaker was a seventeen-year-old boy. He was tall and slender and straight shouldered. His features were finely chiseled. Alexander thought briefly that this was assuredly how Leandro Zapla had looked as a youth. The boy was dressed in rags and was without sandals. His hands were caked with dirt. Some of it was so deeply ingrained in his flesh that a lifetime of washing would never cleanse it away. He was a farmer—a very poor farmer—as were all his relatives who had come down from the loins of Atahualpa.

The excursion to the palace was made late one afternoon. In the distance, rising above groves of willows and fields of wheat, the palace looked beautiful with its crumbling circular towers and walls of granite blocks. But, as the travelers drew up in front of the main entrance, beauty was replaced by a desolation that was pitiful and sinister all at the same time. The trees and flowers and the fields of wheat ended abruptly, as if afraid to come a foot closer to the sprawling mass of broken stone. The ground underfoot turned hard and barren; only weeds had the courage and stamina to thrust their ugly stalks up from the dead earth. The building itself was pitted and streaked with the dust that the centuries had blown against it. From somewhere inside—or was it just imagination?—came the low, anguished moan of the wind. Rubbish was heaped at one end of a flight of steps leading up to the entrance. The steps were chipped and cracked, as were the walls above them. The sun, a disk of blinding yellow, was descending slowly toward the rear of the palace. Its light hurt the eyes and cloaked the already sick colors of the weeds and the broken stone with a lifeless amber, adding to the desolation of the scene.

The travelers followed the boy into the building. Alexander saw courtyards overgrown with weeds, hallways with their stone floors uprooted, and empty rooms whose cracked walls showed clearly where the marauding Spaniards had wrenched down tapestries and intricately designed plates of silver and gold. A cold chill passed through Alexander. It was not caused by the cool, musty air; rather, it came from standing in the presence of power reduced to rot. He glanced at the Inca boy, expecting to find a look of sorrow. Instead, he found eyes glowing with excitement.

"You must not think only of what you see, Excellency. You must think of what you cannot see."

"And what is that?"

The Inca beckoned him to his side. He pointed to the dusty, broken floor stretching away from them on all sides. "The Spanish destroyed the palace. They left it to die. But they did not touch at all the rooms underground. They could not find them. And so the rooms are there today, far beneath our feet, crowded with treasure that would take your breath away."

Aimé was now at Alexander's shoulder. "Rooms? What rooms? Can we see them?"

The Inca shook his head, an expression of wonder growing in his face. "No one may see them. Not even my family —and we are the family of Atahualpa himself. But we know they are there. They are filled with gold and silver, far beyond the amount stolen from our people by the Spanish."

Alexander could see the skepticism in Aimé's face as the Frenchman asked, "Has anyone ever seen them?"

"Oh, yes!" The boy's voice was intense and a little angry, for he, too, had seen the doubt in the Frenchman's face. "A long, long time ago, one of my ancestors covered the eyes of his wife and led her by the hand through many passages to a great underground garden. When he allowed her to see again, she beheld trees of gold laden with leaves and fruits. There were birds perched on their limbs. They were singing the most beautiful songs she had ever heard."

Aimé started to speak, but Alexander stopped him with a thrust of his elbow against his ribs. He wanted nothing to interrupt the boy's recital. He knew he was listening to pure fantasy, to legend born years ago beyond count. He knew he was witnessing the heartbreaking spectacle of youth living on dreams to make present reality more bearable.

The Inca's voice mounted with the vision in his mind.

"She even saw the golden sedan chair of Atahualpa. She stepped forward to touch it—" unconsciously, the boy's hand moved outward in a halting, groping gesture—"but her husband caught her and pulled her away. You see, she could not touch any of the treasures because the day of the return of the Inca nation to power was yet to come and it had been decreed that anyone who touched them before that day should die."

The spell that the story had cast over the boy and that he, in turn, had cast over the room caused Alexander to want to whisper. He managed to say in a normal tone, "Will that day come soon?"

Shining eyes met his.

"Yes, Excellency, very soon."

"When?"

"No one knows. But it will be soon. I feel it in my heart."

For a moment, there was silence. The boy's eyes passed over the three faces before him. Then suddenly—and, it seemed to Alexander, forcibly—his mood changed. He ran lightly, almost gaily, to a corner of the room. Perhaps he was trying to forget that he had seen skepticism and pity in the three faces. Perhaps, in that long moment, he had felt doubt in his own heart. Perhaps some logical part of his Indian brain, a part suffocating beneath all the weight of fantasy and legend, had managed to cry out with chill clarity that his dreams were the dreams of the foolish and the lost. Whatever the reason, he was now all forced gaiety. It had a terrible ring of hollowness to it.

"And over here, Excellency, right beneath my feet, the datura tree grows underground. There is not another like it in the whole world. It is covered with flowers that bloom the whole year round, and its leaves are made of gold wire and plates of gold. Its branches overhang Atahualpa's chair."

Alexander stared at the boy and blinked. The Inca stood by a splitting wall. A shaft of yellow sunlight came through a narrow break in the stone and fell directly upon his face, exaggerating every line and plane in that face. It danced off his eyes and made them glow yellowish and hard. It turned the mouth from a soft, full-lipped line to a string pulled taut. A wind came through the crack, lifted black hair from his shoulders and revealed the corded muscles in his neck; time could not shred those muscles and struggle could not break them. The Indian stood erect, again enveloped in his dream of the wonders underground, and to Alexander he seemed a young god, a young god defiant of his oppressors, waiting for his people to rise again, waiting to take into his hands the power of old.

"Tell me," Alexander asked softly, "do you ever wish to dig for those treasures?"

The boy turned from the wall and the lance of yellow sunlight.

"Oh, no, Excellency. Such a desire never comes to me. My father said it would be sinful. If we had the golden branches with all their golden fruit, our white neighbors would hate and injure us. We have a little field and good wheat."

The golden vigor had fled his face and voice, and with it went the illusion of the young god. He was once again a mere dirt-streaked youth, with his clothes in tatters and his shoulders beginning to sag from his daily labors. He was lost; he would never rise again. His people were lost; they would never rise again.

But, at least, the world would hear of them. History owed them that small service.

And hear of them the world did. Alexander's observations

of the Incas—and of the Aztecs in Mexico—awakened Europe to a recognition of the wonders of a dead age. Slowly came the realization that the peoples of the New World were not barbarians but the products of a rich past. They deserved not condescension but respect.

To his writings and lectures he added a warning to Spain. She must share in this new realization. She was headed for trouble in her New World colonies, he warned, unless she lifted the heel of oppression from her dark-skinned subjects and returned to them their human dignity; the hour was growing late; it was dangerous to continue viewing them as inferior beings.

Spain refused to heed his words and he lived to see revolution sweep the New World.

But the archaeologists and historians of the world listened intently to others of his words. They showed particular interest in his suspicion that the native peoples of the New World had originally come from Asia. He backed up his theory with sound observations—the similarities between the calendric systems and religious myths of the Orientals and the ancient South Americans, and the odd resemblance between temple design in Yucatan and Guatemala and that in India. Of all his Indian observations, these pleased him the most. He now sensed that there was not only a harmony existing among the inanimate objects in nature but also a harmony among the civilizations of the world.

Alexander was to live to see many of the fruits of his Inca and Aztec investigations. He was to know that he had inspired the first anthropologic studies of South America, the initial steps taken along a trail that is still being pursued today—a trail that in some future day may lead definitely from the earliest peoples of the Western Hemisphere to the earliest peoples of the Eastern Hemisphere. And he was to live to hear himself called the "first archaeologist of South America."

The days moved swiftly after Cajamarca. The travelers came down out of the mountains to Trujillo and silently viewed for the first time the Pacific Ocean and told themselves that Balboa could have felt no greater awe "upon a peak in Darien" on that September day nearly three centuries ago.

From Trujillo their route carried them south to Callao, the port for the city of Lima. Alexander was to remember Callao with amusement throughout his life. It was while stopping there that he learned that a substance called *guano*, the droppings of coastal birds, had been used for years in the area as fertilizer. He collected samples and had them shipped to France for study. The results of the study turned the eyes of every European farmer to the western coast of South America; guano, it was found, was extremely rich in phosphates and nitrogen, so rich, in fact, that one ton of the material could do the work of thirty-three tons of ordinary fertilizer. In his later years, when guano was being shipped to all parts of Europe and the United States, Alexander, who had realized no profit for his efforts, was to smile and observe wryly, "Everyone thought gold and silver the most important products of South America. Now they have found a more precious substance."

The explorers remained in Lima for seven weeks, disliking the town intensely. It was a cold place, socially and physically. The townspeople were silent and haughty and forever looking down their noses at their visitors. And the city was blanketed in fog from the sea for almost every day of their stay there. Fortunately, it cleared in time for Alexander to watch the transit of Mercury across the face of the sun, an observation that contributed greatly to the understanding by astronomy of that planet's orbit.

The explorers departed from Lima aboard the frigate *Atlante* on December 5, 1802. The ship swung northward towards Mexico. The coast of Peru slipped by the starboard rail and fell away over the stern quarter, disappearing forever from Alexander's view.

Ahead, far to the north and east of Mexico, lay a new and lasting friendship.

CHAPTER TWELVE

The Red-Headed American

It was a morning of mist in Philadelphia, on that day of May 24, 1804, a mist that was more white than gray. It stood along Broad and Market streets and was cool against the faces of the shopkeepers throwing wide their shutters and doors; it cloaked the ships berthed all along the eastern bank of the Delaware and gave their bare masts a look of softness and slackened their rigging with its dampness. The mist was a relaxing rather than a depressing thing. It muted the continual bang of the hammers over in the shipyards and made strollers of a people who happily admitted that they were conscientious bustlers.

A frigate came slowly into its slip near the Schuylkill that morning. In the faces of its passengers, lining the rails to hail dock workers and the sailors on neighboring ships, were expressions of relief. They were twenty-six days out of Havana, twenty-six days of vicious storms that had carried away a royal yard and stove in the side of a ship's boat. To the passengers, Philadelphia was the most beautiful spot on earth. It is not unfair to the city to say that they would have viewed any safe anchorage, even a cove in a deserted Pacific island, in exactly the same fashion.

Among the passengers crowding the rails were Alexander, Aimé, and Carlos Montúfar. They stood shoulder to shoulder in silence, each reacting to the city of the Quakers in his own way.

To Carlos, the mist was like that of Lima, though not so thick and not shot through with the odor of salt and wet sand. But there all similarity ended. For all he knew, this city might well have been on another planet. There was not a single adobe house in sight; not a native cart; not a shawled duenna with her young charge gliding along in a volante; not one Indian in his tattered but colorful costume. Here were brick buildings, their reds turning black from smoke. Here were men in black broadcloth suits and flat, broad-brimmed hats. Here were dock workers in loose-fitting homespun. And here were faces that were all pink and white. Indeed, it was a city on another planet—and he loved it.

As for Alexander, he was peering at the brick buildings looming through the mist, but he was not seeing them so much as he was feeling the history that gripped them. It was a good history, as refreshing as the morning; this was the city in which had been plotted a government that would not oppress the people but free them. And it was a history as new as the morning; somewhere over there in the mist was the very neat—almost prim—Independence Hall where, within his own memory, the Declaration of Independence had been signed; and, because they had been alive almost the day before yesterday, fresh in the mind of the world were the men who had made the war against England—Washington, the roly-poly Ben Franklin (remember, the explorer told himself, when you insisted his lightning rod be installed atop Tegel), Hancock, Putnam, Gates, and Marion. And the history was as hopeful as the morning; it had shown the whole world that the weak and the strong, the proud and the humble, the good and the bad, the brilliant and the stupid, the courageous and the frightened could, by combining their wills and their brains, construct a system of living beneficial to all.

Alexander had given up the idea of exploring Canada and then the Mississippi. His journey to North America was a pilgrimage to the young history of the United States. He wanted to see a land without serfdom, a land without scars left by marching, marauding conquistadors, a land dedicated to freedom and bewildered by the slavery existing in its southern extremities, a land that depended on something besides the pomp of palaces and the gaudy splendor of uniforms for its pride. And he wanted to see one of the men responsible for the establishment of that land.

Standing next to Alexander, Aimé regarded the city with open relief. Because he was French, he could not keep his feelings to himself. "I never thought we would get here! I would not have wagered a sou that we would ever touch dry land again!"

Alexander grinned at the botanist. "You thought we would end up at the bottom of the sea off the Bahamas, eh? But you weren't afraid for yourself, were you? It was your precious plants that worried you."

"Do you blame me? *I* can swim. But my lovely plants cannot." The botanist jabbed a large forefinger at Alexander's chest. "I did not spend all those months in the Andes and Mexico collecting them just to feed them to some fishes."

"Well, I hadn't a single worry," Alexander said, meaning it. "I knew we had come too far for anything to happen to us. Let the storms come. The Atlantic can do as its pleases. We'll be safe in Paris before the year is out."

There was a long scraping sound as the ship came up against the wharf. The faces of dock workers grinned up at the travelers. Ropes snaked out from bow and stern. The journey that had commenced fourteen months ago at Lima was done.

Fourteen months? Alexander asked himself. It hardly seemed possible to think that Peru was more than a year in the past. So much had happened to give time wings.

First, en route from Lima to Acapulco, he had measured the temperature and flow of the cold Pacific current governing the climate along the western face of South America. It had been a study that one day would cause him concern; geographers would mistakenly credit him with the discovery of the current and attach to it his name, driving him to argue again and again that he had not discovered but merely studied an ocean river "known since the sixteenth century to every sailor-boy accustomed to navigate between Chili and Payta." But his arguments would go in vain. The name, Humboldt Current, would remain on the maps of the world.

Mexico had proved to be a long march of triumphs for the explorer. First, he had corrected the geographical location of the seaport of Acapulco. Then, in Mexico City, he had added to his knowledge of ancient American civilizations through a study of the Aztec nation, and had informed government officials of the latest European mining techniques, information that would be incorporated into that country's far flung silver operations. Finally, in the autumn of 1803, he had climbed his last New World volcano—Jorullo, near Uruapan, a smoking monster that had been born in 1759, thrusting its cone up to a height of fifteen hundred feet in the course of one night and spewing out such heat that a nearby river had evaporated within minutes. Tenerife. Cotopaxi. Pichincha. Chimborazo. Jorullo. The explorer had climbed them all—and many more—with the result that soon he would give the world a new kind of map, a map of volcanoes, and he would startle the realm of geology with the information that volcanoes fell into linear formations across the face of the earth and that they corresponded with vast underground fissures.

After a winter spent in Mexico City, the travelers had moved on to Vera Cruz and then across the Caribbean to Cuba. There, they had remained just long enough to pick up the crate of plant specimens left behind in 1801 and to book passage on a frigate to the United States.

And now here they were, walking down a trembling gangway to the wharf at Philadelphia. They were on the last leg of their New World journey. They strolled slowly past the warehouses, stores, and narrow ropewalks forming a high fence between the city and the dock, and they felt as though they were on a vacation. No longer was it necessary to dash into the woods to gather plants or produce the sextant and chronometer to correct the geographical position of a site. They merely had to enjoy themselves. They were no longer explorers—just tourists.

However, Alexander did have one task he was eager to perform. He sat down to it as soon as he and his companions had settled themselves in an inn on Market Street. He took up a pen and wrote a letter to the man he had come to the United States to see. The letter was addrssed to Thomas Jefferson, President of the United States.

> "Mr. President:
>
> Arrived from Mexico on the blessed ground of this republic, whose executive powers were placed in your hands, I feel it my pleasant duty to present my respects and express my high admiration for your writings, your actions, and the liberalism of your ideas, which have inspired me from my earliest youth. I flatter myself in the expectation of express-

ing my sentiments orally to you, remitting at the same time the attached parcel, which my friend the Consul of the United States in Havana asked me to send to you. . . .

"For moral reasons I could not resist seeing the United States and enjoying the consoling aspects of a people who understand the precious gift of Liberty. I hope to be able to present my personal respects and admiration to one who contemplates philosophically the troubles of two continents. . . . I would love to talk to you about a subject that you have treated so ingeniously in your work on Virginia, the teeth of mammoth which we too discovered in the Andes. . . ."

When he had sealed the envelope and dispatched it by fast horse to Washington, he grinned at Aimé. "I have just invited myself to the presidential mansion. I hope Jefferson will have time to see me."

"I think he'll find the time," Aimé said. "I have an idea you're going to find yourself quite famous all over the world. Four years in South America. That's quite a feat." To prove his opinion, Aimé held out a calling card. "You're in Philadelphia less than an hour and there's a gentleman downstairs to see you."

The gentleman proved to be Charles Willson Peale, a friend of Jefferson's. An energetic man in his fifties, he shook Alexander's hand warmly and insisted on the privilege of showing him the sights of Philadelphia. "I'm afraid, though, that the honor won't be solely mine. We'll soon be joined by others."

The "others" were the Reverend Mr. Nicholas Collin and Dr. Anthony Fothergill. "Put yourselves in our hands, gentlemen," was their advice. "Philadelphia is yet a small city, surely not as grand as Havana, but one worth seeing, and remembering, for it is the birthplace of the United States."

And so, while awaiting a reply from Jefferson, the three

travelers gave themselves over to their self-appointed American guides. They tramped along brick and dirt streets from one end of Philadelphia to another, entering modest Independence Hall with its white tower and delicate little clock, pausing before Christ Church to gaze up at its simple but dignified steeple, and lingering before Philosophical Hall to hear the Reverend Mr. Collin remark, "In the event that some Europeans still think of Americans as country bumpkins, you might point out to them that you saw on the edge of a wilderness a building dedicated to science. In there, Joseph Priestley discussed the discovery of oxygen and Ben Franklin lectured on electricity."

The reply from Jefferson reached Alexander at the end of the month. It set him to grinning like a child. Jefferson had written:

Washington: May 28, 1804

Sir,—I received last night your favor of the 24th, and offer you my congratulations on your arrival here in good health after a tour in the course of which you have been exposed to many hardships and hazards. The countries you have visited are those least known and most interesting, and a lively desire will be felt generally to receive the information you will be able to give. No one will feel it more strongly than myself, because no one perhaps views this New World with more partial hopes for its exhibiting an ameliorated state of the human condition. In the new position in which the seat of our government is fixed, we have nothing curious to attract the observation of a traveller, and can only substitute in its place the welcome with which we should receive your visit, should you find it convenient to add so much to your journey. Accept, I pray you, my respectful salutations and assurances of great respect and consideration, &c.

Jefferson

Alexander read the latter part of the letter a second time, particularly the line, "should you find it convenient to add so much to your journey." He laughed aloud. He had worried himself that the President of the United States might not have the time to see him. And now here was Jefferson wondering if he, Humboldt, would find it convenient to visit the capital. How different this was from the command of a European king to appear at court.

Travel arrangements were quickly made. Peale, Collin, and Fothergill would not think of allowing their guests to make the journey alone. Consequently, the morning stage bound for Washington via Baltimore was reserved for a party of six.

The coach rolled into Washington at noon of a humid June day. The city was a depressing sight, as it was at any time of any day in that year of 1804. Glancing out the window of the moving carriage, Alexander understood the comment he had so often heard back in Philadelphia whenever he had let it be known he planned to visit the capital: "Why in thunderation a country in its right mind ever chose to put the seat of government in that God-forsaken spot, I'll never know!" Swamps stretched away on all sides of the sagging wood houses at the edge of the city. In the town itself, the streets were wide, but muddy and pocked with chuckholes full of water. Most of the newer homes were without lawns and hedges, and the outhouses and pumps in the backyards were visible from the street. But, circling in the distance, were the half-complete Capitol building of Virginia sandstone, the Treasury Building, and the presidential mansion. They stood stark and bare against the sky, a presage of an architectural dignity yet to come.

"Lovely place," Peale growled. "We should have left it to the Indians. I've known Tom Jefferson for years, but I think he was six sorts of fool to swing his weight to set the capital down here." He leaned across to Alexander and tapped his knee. "Wait until you see Pennsylvania Avenue. One hundred and sixty feet wide, it is. But as rough as a wilderness trail. When it snows, you can't get from the president's house to the Capitol building."

"It might look better if there were some trees about," Collin said, a little defensively. "Jefferson says he's going to plant poplars down Pennsylvania Avenue to Washington's monument."

"What monument? They've been talking about putting Washington on that stone horse for years, but so far no one's done a thing about it," Fothergill grumbled.

"Well, no matter what is done to this town, no one will ever be able to say that Congress was in its right mind when it made its choice. We're the first country in the world to be able to design a capital city from scratch." Peale waved his hand disgustedly at the passing scene. "And this is what we've got."

Collin was still on the defensive. "But it was a good plan. I saw it once. It was drawn up by that Frenchman who was with Washington in the Revolution. A major. What was his name?"

"L'Enfant," Fothergill helped.

"Pierre l'Enfant," Peale said.

"Well, he drew up a nice set of plans. Quite lovely, really."

"He was wasting his time," Peale announced. "Take my word for it, we will move this whole thing out of here—lock, stock, and barrel—one of these days."

The carriage entered Pennsylvania Avenue. Several minutes later, it clattered up a curving drive to the presidential mansion. It was a simple two-story building with a look of an English manor about it. An Ionic portico and balustrade graced its front. Alexander, accustomed to the splendor of

European palaces and the rambling nature of Spanish American mansions, was struck by the smallness of the building. Too, he was interested in the blend of youth and age that it had achieved. The ground sweeping down to Pennsylvania Avenue was bright with freshly planted grass, but the Washington climate was already eating at the building itself, giving it a weathered appearance. When, in 1814, it would receive its first coat of white paint to cover the scars left by the fire set by British troops, he would smile and think, "It certainly needed it."

The travelers were greeted by a young Army officer who escorted them into the house. They followed his straight back along a carpeted hall, moving past ornately furnished rooms to the door of the presidential office. There, they were turned over to another officer, a colonel, who, upon hearing their names, smiled and said, "Ah, yes, the President is expecting you. Won't you be seated, please?"

The officer disappeared through the door at his back. He was gone just long enough to give the six men a chance to arrange their travel-wrinkled clothes. Then he was in the doorway, standing very erect and saying, "The President will see you now."

Alexander was the first of the party to step past him. The office he entered was bright with sunlight and, coming toward him from behind a polished desk, was a sandy-haired man in his early sixties. The man gave his Army aide no chance for a formal introduction.

"Baron von Humboldt? May I bid you welcome?"

The European-trained Alexander came close to bowing. He was prevented from doing so by a large hand that swept forward and took his. "My congratulations on your long and interesting journey. I've a great many questions to ask you."

After the introductions of Aimé and Carlos had been performed and after the sandy-haired man had greeted their

American companions, the visitors accepted chairs about the polished desk and Alexander had his first opportunity to take a long look at this man who had become a legend in his own lifetime—Thomas Jefferson, Virginia gentleman, revolutionary, author of the Declaration of Independence, onetime American Minister to France, Secretary of State under George Washington, and the possessor of one of the most brilliant minds of the age, a mind capable of embracing with equal ease such widely diverse interests as geography, agriculture, geology, botany, surgery, literature, and religion.

All the way down from Philadelphia, the explorer had wondered what sort of man he would find here in the house on Pennsylvania Avenue. Would he find a fiery intellectual? There was real anger behind the formal phrasing of the Declaration of Independence and deep passion in the Jefferson statement of four years ago, "I have sworn on the altar of God eternal hostility against every form of tyranny over the mind of man." Despite the warmth of Jefferson's invitation, would he find a man too preoccupied with affairs of state to spend more than a few polite and fleeting minutes with his guests? Only last year Jefferson had completed the Louisiana Purchase and was at this moment wondering what the explorers Lewis and Clark would find on the march he had instructed them to take to the Pacific coast. Or—as Fothergill had warned—would he find a man cold to strangers?

What he saw was a man who looked as if he would be more at home in the outdoors than in an executive mansion. The President was extremely tall—six feet two inches—and large-boned, so large-boned in fact that he looked ungainly as he rounded the polished desk and took to his chair. His face, too, was large, with a square chin, prominent nose, and flattish cheeks. Sandy hair fell in a straight line across his forehead and, waving slightly, slipped down over his ears; in earlier days, the hair had been thick, but now it was growing sparse about the crown of his head. There were deep lines at the corners of his mouth and flecks of hazel in his gray eyes. His skin looked hard to the touch and his complexion was ruddy.

Slowly, as Jefferson questioned him about his South American travels and then listened attentively to his answers, the explorer felt his fears of the past days dissolve in the face of reality. Jefferson was not cold to strangers; rather, he had about him a quietness—perhaps even a shyness—that could easily be mistaken for aloofness. Nor was he just being polite to a visitor to his country. He was genuinely interested in what his guest was saying. And—this Alexander had never doubted—the man was brilliant. He had a mind capable of grasping point after point with the speed of a steel trap closing.

The explorer had a chance really to view that mind at work at dinner that night. Jefferson set his guests a lavish table, but the meal was without the ceremony of foreign gatherings. There was not the customary, fatiguing round of toasts and, when the President had settled himself at the head of the table, he glanced at his guests with a grave sort of humor from beneath sandy brows and remarked, "I think we can do without talk of politics this evening. It doesn't mix well with good food."

Then, prompted by a curious Alexander, he swept with lightning swiftness over a wide variety of subjects.

Of agriculture, he said:

"America hasn't even guessed its farming potential yet. There is much fine food grown in Europe that would do well, I'm sure, in this nation's soil. Someday—when I have the time—I'm of a mind to plant French grapes, and Italian rice and olives at Monticello."

Of slavery:

"I want to see it gone from these shores. So do some of

the best minds we have—Secretary of State Madison, for one. I have fought against it since as far back as 1769. And it will depart. Mark my words, it will depart. Slowly but surely."

Of the people:

"I'm afraid I trust their honesty and common sense completely. A country need not shackle them to survive. It has only to appeal to their reason."

Of education:

"I want to see an educational system that will reach every child in America. I want to see the poor educated. I want to see free state colleges and a free state library. Education is not the privilege of the rich and middle class.

Of the future:

"Every man is as sovereign as the country in which he lives. George III and the Revolution taught us how precious that sovereignty is. We will flourish as a nation only so long as we recognize and cherish and nurture that individual sovereignty."

Alexander listened intently, smiling constantly. Here was a mind producing the sort of language he had always wanted to hear from the highest seat in government. Here was a language that spoke of a future free from the chains of slavery and without the deafening tramp of conquering armies. He knew he was one of the very few men in the world who, upon meeting a human legend, was not disappointed by it.

He was delighted when, at the end of the meal, Jefferson invited him to his office for a last glass of wine.

With a decanter in hand, the President inquired of the explorer, "How long do you anticipate remaining in the United States?"

"We have no definite schedule, Mr. President. I imagine our departure will be an early one, though. We have a staggering amount of material to be classified and put into written form. I'm afraid several years of hard work are ahead of us."

"And many honors. You're bound for Paris?"

"Yes."

Jefferson smiled, passing a wine glass to Alexander. "If I know Paris, she will welcome you with open arms. I don't think there's a city anywhere in the world that appreciates a scholar more." He studied his own glass for a moment. "I hope, however, that you will not be leaving too soon. You can be of great service to this country—and to me personally."

"Yes?"

"As you know, we have just completed the purchase of the territory of Louisiana from the French. For the sum of fifteen million dollars, we have obtained one million square miles of land. You understand, of course, what this means to us?"

Alexander nodded. "The size of your country has doubled."

"Overnight," Jefferson added. He set aside his glass and leaned back against the desk, folding his arms. "And it means much more to us. It has brought our borders down to the Gulf and over to the borders of Mexico. If we are to live side by side with the countries to the south, we must learn all we can of them. With your experience, I think you would make an excellent teacher."

"I don't know how excellent I shall prove," a pleased Humboldt replied. "But I assure you I shall be a willing one. Whatever information I have is at your disposal."

Alexander's duties as a teacher were to keep him in the United States until July. His classrooms were to be the executive mansion, the office of the Secretary of the Treasury, Albert Gallatin, and Jefferson's home, Monticello.

He presented to the Swiss-born Gallatin for copying all his maps and notes on the production and natural resources of the Spanish colonies to the south, plus a wealth of information delivered orally and at such a rate that Gallatin later observed that he had "swallowed more information of various kinds in less than two hours than I had for the past two years read and heard."

At the executive mansion and later at Monticello, Alexander provided facts on Mexico's northern provinces to be used in Jefferson's report to Congress on the Louisiana Purchase. At the end of one session, Jefferson told him in that slow, thoughtful voice of his, "If we are going to succeed in building a country from coast to coast—and that's what it's coming to, for certain—we must know the extent of our natural resources. You have given us the beginning clue. For that I am personally grateful to you."

An association that had started on a basis of mutual admiration slowly blossomed into an abiding friendship, and came to full flower at Jefferson's magnificent—but so often disheveled—home at Monticello. There, free of the pressures of Washington, the two men were able to come to know each other intimately. And there, daily, Alexander saw some new facet of the complex Jefferson personality.

He had only to watch the man with his two surviving daughters and his grandchildren to know that he was a devoted family man; for a moment, the explorer felt a strange little twinge of envy: family life—that was something that he knew would never be his. He wondered how Fothergill could ever have thought Jefferson a cold, an aloof personality. For all his shyness and quiet manner, the man loved to surround himself with his friends. Monticello, as carefully as its surrounding gardens were maintained and as tastefully as its rooms were furnished, was not beyond the danger of the master's ordering as many as fifty beds set up to accommodate guests who had been persuaded—without too much difficulty—to remain a few days that often turned into many weeks.

The explorer came to look upon this third President of the United States as the nineteenth century personification of Aristotle's "well rounded man." Jefferson rode as if he had been born in the saddle, a trait he shared with his late fellow Virginian, George Washington. He had a deep interest in literature, his tastes running to Molière and *Don Quixote,* and he had already proved his ability as an author with the Declaration of Independence and his pre-Revolutionary pamphlet, *A Summary View of the Rights of America.* Possibly his only irritating trait was his love of playing the violin. Scraping, Alexander considered it; not because Jefferson was an inadequate musician but simply because music itself bored Alexander beyond belief.

But this fault was easily forgotten once Jefferson began to talk about science. The President was a man of the laboratory through and through. "Do you know," Alexander told Aimé and Carlos, "that he has been experimenting for years with crop rotation at Monticello? For more than ten years, he has received annually from the superintendent of the Jardin des Plantes in Paris boxes of seed which he has distributed to farmers throughout these states for experimental cultivation. He has gone on geological surveys here and abroad, and while he was serving as Minister to France he spent his spare time taking meteorologic observations."

While at Monticello, Alexander became a pupil as well as a teacher. He turned to a study of the political system of the United States, surveying not only the broad principles on which it was founded but delving into its minor details as well, and going so far as to institute a comparison between conditions in this new nation and those of the Spanish colonies. The results of the study and the comparison rounded out his already firm conviction that the hope of the world lay in this land. Freedom, with its foothold on these northern shores, had the opportunity to demonstrate for the world how the gift of his dignity released in man the energies necessary for the betterment of himself and his nation. Surely, when that demonstration was complete, freedom would sweep southward. And then, perhaps, eastward to those many countries in Europe where the knee was still bent to kings and emperors.

Had he been able to look into the future, he would have discovered that he would live to see the flames of freedom swing in that southward and then that eastward direction.

Jefferson himself gave the explorer his final lesson of life in a democracy late in Alexander's stay at Monticello. The lesson was a simple one, the manner of its presentation somewhat comical, and the incident that gave it birth trivial. But it was representative of a whole way of life to Alexander and he carried the memory of it with pleasure for the remainder of his days.

One morning, as the explorer was seated at breakfast, Jefferson appeared suddenly in the dining room door. His hair was awry and he was wearing a dressing gown. He had been upstairs in his bedroom going over the newspapers sent him from Washington and he held in his hand a press clipping. He threw it down on the table in front of Alexander.

"Look at that, my friend."

The explorer's brows arched in surprise and shock as he read the clipping. It was a vehement attack on the President and his administration and was couched in the roughest terms possible. When he had finished his reading of it, he cast it aside and then looked up to find Jefferson grinning broadly.

"How can you smile at a thing like that?" he demanded.

Jefferson did not answer the question directly. Instead, he picked up the clipping and returned it to Alexander. "Take it home with you. Exhibit it in a museum. Let it show those monarchs who are afraid of a free press just how little they really have to fear."

"But this is enough to get an editor's head lopped off in France."

"That's France. This is America. I am hit like this every day. Yet I don't fear it because the people do their own thinking. They must—for my administration has never been more popular. Take it with you, please. Remember it as a symbol of this nation."

Alexander looked at the clipping again. He could not agree with what it said, but, like the target of its attack, he had to admit that it was a symbol of the kind of country he had come to see.

And Jefferson, standing there in his wrinkled dressing gown with his hair awry, and laughing at this personal attack and trusting in the intelligence of the people—that, somehow, was a fitting farewell from this man of democracy.

On July 9, 1804, the frigate, *La Favorite,* raised sail and moved down the Delaware from Philadelphia to the Atlantic.

Standing at her rail that day were Alexander, Aimé, and Carlos. Silently, as the great ship cut its way efficiently eastward, they watched the shoreline of the United States drop low against the sea in the distance.

Each man was lost in his own thoughts there at the rail. Carlos was happily anticipating his first look at Europe; Aimé was counting the days to a reunion with his brother; and Alexander was thinking ahead about mountains—the mountains of paper work that awaited him.

For Humboldt the thrill of the future was tempered by a strange sense of hollowness somewhere deep within him. He was leaving a part of the world to which he had given five years of his life. He was leaving a country he loved more than his own. He was leaving a man who had come to be one of his closest friends, a man with whom he would correspond for the rest of his life.

With that sudden, frightening clarity that so often rises out of a moment of quiet sadness, he knew he would never again see Jefferson, the United States, and South America. No matter where he traveled in the future, his path would never lead him back to the New World. The work that had to be done on these shores would now be done by others.

The three men watched the fading shoreline all the day. At sunset, it was hazy and purple on the horizon. By the following morning, it was gone. There was only the empty sea all around them.

CHAPTER THIRTEEN

Paris and the Corsican Corporal

THE COACH FROM BORDEAUX clattered into a Paris caught in a happy turmoil that day of August 18, 1804. Hot sunlight poured out of the sky, and spirited conversation danced along the streets. Everyone—the poor in the alleys of La Chapelle, the fashionable strolling the Boulevard des Italiens, and the merchants in their shops near Chaumont—was discussing the wonderful party the city had given three days ago to mark the first public celebration of Napoleon Bonaparte's birthday. Hadn't the Tuileries looked magnificent with all its windows ablaze with light? Hadn't the singing and dancing in the streets reached an unexcelled gaiety? And hadn't the troops of Bonaparte seemed invincible as they paraded beneath the glitter of their bayonets and the bright colors of the flags and banners swirling by the thousands from windows and rooftops?

Then the glow in the eyes of the speakers deepened and their hands gestured with greater abandon as they talked of yet another party, a party to be held within three months, a party to put that glorious one just concluded to shame. Napoleon had recently overthrown the Revolutionary Directorate and had startled the entire nation with the announcement that France was no longer a republic but a monarchy and that he was to be its Emperor, adding that his coronation would take place in November. Already workmen were converging on the Île de la Cîté to adorn the cathedral of Notre Dame for the ceremonies, and already foreign delegations were preparing for a dignified trek to Paris. And the Vatican was involved. Napoleon was insisting that the crown of France be placed on his head by the Pope and that the task be performed in Paris, not Rome. The Pope was hesitating, replying that Bonaparte should come to him. But Parisians had no fear concerning his ultimate decision. He would come to Notre Dame. The Vicar of Christ—like the rest of the world—had learned that the little fellow who lived with his Creole wife at the Tuileries invariably had his own way in the end.

The idea of this approaching festival held no thrill for the older of the two men in the carriage now swinging out of the Place d'Italie and clattering up the Boulevard de l'Hôpital. Alexander thought moodily of how much France had changed in the past five years. When last he had been here she had been a republic, freshly released from the prison of monarchy. Now her affairs had turned in a full circle. She was a monarchy again. A dynasty of Napoleons was being established. The guillotine of the Place de la Révolution was forgotten, and the banners of freedom were torn and cast aside in the dust of history.

The carriage halted before the Jardin des Plantes. The Seine sparkled in the sunlight just beyond the Quay St. Bernard, but Alexander had time for no more than a glimpse of the river, for a group of dark-suited men gathered eagerly about the carriage door. All of them seemed to speak at once. A smile broke over his face as the explorer recognized many of their number. They were representatives from the Jardin des Plantes, the University of Paris, the Institut National, and the Observatoire, all come to bid him welcome.

He stepped down to the group. His hands were grasped from all quarters. He felt his shoulders being patted repeatedly and experienced peculiar tightening in his throat at the display of warm friendship. He managed to introduce Carlos Montúfar before a wave of questions engulfed him:

"All your plant specimens are safe, Baron?"

"Your voyage home was pleasant? Indeed? Only twenty-seven days? Remarkable!"

"You will be staying with us for sometime, will you not? The Observatoire is most eager to study your barometric readings."

"And, pray, where is Monsieur Bonpland? We expected to see him."

To that inquiry, Alexander replied, "He has gone to visit his brother at La Rochelle. But have no fear, he will be in Paris within a few weeks. Perhaps days. He cannot bear to remain away from his precious plants too. . . ."

It was then that he glanced over the heads of the men and saw the young woman with the dark hair. At first, he stared in surprise; she was the last person he had expected to encounter in Paris. Then his smile broadened and, with a soft, "You must excuse me, gentlemen," he moved swiftly through the circling dark coats to her. She came into his arms without a word. He held her for a long moment, then stepped back, gripping her shoulders.

"Li! How wonderful to see you! You haven't changed a bit. You are still the most beautiful sister-in-law in all the world!"

Caroline von Humboldt had yet to speak. She gazed at

the explorer, tears shining in her eyes, and so taken by his presence that she was quite unaware that their embrace had tipped her bright bonnet far back on her head. Alexander knew she was trying to accustom herself to a man far different from the one she had last seen more than five years ago. The person who had said farewell to her in Paris had been an ambitious youth, eager for travel, frustrated by a life without exploration. The Humboldt who had returned to her was a bronzed and mature man, exuding the confidence and self-satisfaction of an ambition realized. The tears in her dark eyes brightened and then came down her cheeks. She pressed herself to him, crying against his chest,

"Oh, Alex! How many times we all thought you were dead! There were so many terrible reports."

He threw back his head and laughed. It was exactly the thing a woman would say, even before she had asked you how you were. He cupped her face in his hands, losing his fingers in the dark folds of her hair. "I know. I've heard all about them. But I'm alive. And as healthy as can be. You can see for yourself—"

She hurried on, unmindful of his male logic, "Once, the papers said you had been lost in a shipwreck. Then another reported you had died of fever."

"Well, you can forget them all. I'm back again—safe and well." Then he remembered his surprise at seeing her. "But I didn't expect you here in Paris." He looked about swiftly. "Is it possible Wilhelm is with you? Did you both come up from Rome to bid me welcome?"

He saw a sudden grayness beneath her high color. And then he noticed the darkish stains that had been below her eyes the entire time. Caroline shook her head, biting her lip to hold back fresh tears. "No. He's still at Rome, still representing Germany at the Vatican."

Alexander frowned at the fresh tears. He studied his sister-in-law closely, seeing things about her that he had been too excited to see before. She had lost much weight since their last meeting. And she had grown older; that was to be expected—five years was a long time; but, on the other hand, he sensed her look of oldness had nothing to do with age.

"What is it, Li? What's wrong? Is there trouble between you and Wilhelm?"

Caroline shook her head. "Oh, no! It's nothing like that. We're closer together than ever before. We have to be." The grayness in her face was quite pronounced now. "But, of course, you couldn't have heard. Her voice broke as she spoke the name of her oldest child.

"Is he ill?"

"He was." She tried to continue, but failed. She had no need to continue. Alexander understood.

"Li, I'm so sorry. When did it happen?"

"Several months ago. It was all very sudden. One day he was perfectly well and the next day he was down with a fever. Wilhelm insisted I come to Paris. He said it would do me good." Her hand came to her mouth and pressed itself hard against her lips in a small fist. Her face was breaking, torn between anger and anguish. "It sounds so terrible, doesn't it—that I should be enjoying myself here while my little boy lies—"

Alexander caught her arms and shook her gently but firmly.

"Stop that sort of talk, my dear. This instant. It won't give you back your child and it won't give you back your health."

He saw her take hold of herself. He knew she wasn't following his advice; that sort of advice was always useless. Rather, she seemed to be saying to herself that she had no right—not even that of a bereaved parent—to darken for him this day of homecoming. She began fussing with the folds of his stock, blinking her eyes to clear away the tears. "I have rented an apartment for you. There will be room in it for your friend. It's in the very same building as mine. Remember how I was always saying I wanted to make a real home for you? Well, I am going to have my chance at last." She stepped back, surveyed him, in full control of herself once again. "Now, please introduce me to your young companion so that I can play my part in making your welcome home complete. I want you to enjoy every minute of Paris."

Alexander squeezed her arm. "Have no fear, Li. I have looked forward to Paris for five years. If I have earned any glory, I am going to bask in it to my heart's content."

Though he had spoken lightly of his intention, Caroline von Humboldt soon realized that her brother-in-law had meant it very seriously. She had taken great pains in preparing his apartment, even moving in some of her own china and bric-à-brac for an added touch of home, but, for all the interest in the place that Alexander displayed, she might well have spared herself the effort. To him, it was a convenient headquarters for bathing, changing clothes, and snatching a few hours' sleep.

He hurried everywhere during those first weeks in Paris —to the Jardin des Plantes to uncrate and begin the classification of the plant specimens; to the Observatoire to set the scientists there to the task of reviewing his barometric readings; to the Bureau of Longitude Studies to put his astronomical observations in order prior to the monumental job of incorporating them in the maps of the world.

The nights found him in the homes of the Paris great; he was feted endlessly, questioned incessantly on his travels, and engulfed in a rising tide of admiration. Wherever he went in the city, he was recognized; tailors bowed him into their shops; waiters deserted other diners to hurry to his table; ambitious mothers halted their carriages to introduce their sometimes embarrassed, sometimes equally ambitious and always giggling daughters and to press upon him invitations to dinner. He could not open a newspaper without finding his name somewhere in one of its columns. Paris—a city that so dearly loved the extraordinary—had taken him into her arms and he was accepting her adoration eagerly. He accepted it without blaming himself. Had not he worked hard for all the adulation, all the attention, all the respect? The bouquet of fame was in his hands at last after five years of jungle life and he planned to savor its fragrance as deeply as possible.

Caroline watched him with growing concern as August slipped into September and September into October. She felt two distinct fears for him. First, she was concerned about his looks. The long hours of work followed by the longer hours of play were turning his bronzed complexion a pasty gray. Hard little lines were showing about his mouth, and there were purplish smudges along his lower lids. She remembered him as an animated conversationalist, but now there was more than animation in his voice and more than high spirits in his gestures. There was nervousness. The nervousness of fatigue.

"You are doing too much," she told him one night upon returning to his apartment from a banquet. "Really, Alex, you must take care of yourself."

"Nonsense. I have never felt better in my life."

"But your health—you know yourself it never was very good."

"My dear, I gave up worrying about my health years ago. On a mountainside, it was. I must tell you about it sometime." He had been pulling off his coat as he talked. Now he threw it carelessly over the back of a chair and made for a table littered with papers.

"You are not going to work *now?*" Caroline cried.

"But of course I am."

"But, Alex! Really! Be sensible." She had one hand on her hip and the other was pointing to the clock on the mantel. "It's after two in the morning. How many hours did you sleep last night?"

He shrugged absently. He was rummaging among the papers on the table. "Three hours. Perhaps four."

"And how many hours the night before last?"

"I really don't remember."

She went to him and turned him about and cried angrily up into his face, "Well, I do! I heard your carriage arrive. It was four o'clock. Just before daybreak. Alex, you can't go on this way. You are killing yourself.

He waved a sheaf of papers under her nose. His eyes were bright with the memory of the affair they had just attended, an affair that had all but genuflected to him. "Li, darling, you are being an awful pest. I'm not killing myself. And if I do—which I won't—then I will have all eternity for sleeping. Right now, I haven't the time for sleeping. I have got to put these notes in order. I promised to show them to the members of the Institut National tomorrow."

"The notes and the Institut can wait. You must get some rest."

He threw back his head and laughed. "The Institut cannot wait! Nor can the notes. They're very special notes. Look." He pulled her to the table, a little boy ready to show off a remarkable toy he had constructed.

"So you think I have been too busy these past weeks? Why, Li, the work is just beginning." He cleared a space on the table and spread several sheets of paper on it. "I started these notes in Mexico. I have spent the past nights refining them."

"Mornings, you mean," she said icily.

"Mornings. Nights. It makes no difference." He pointed to the notes, at the same time shaking her arm with good-humored impatience. "Look at them, Li. Do you know what they are?"

Caroline stared at the papers. She wrinkled her nose. "My dear, only a magician could decipher your handwriting. I'm afraid I'm not a magician."

"It's a list of the books I am going to write on South America. Listen." He bent far over for a better look at the papers, the palms of his hands supporting him against the edge of the table. "I shall start with a general account of my travels, a sort of introduction that will touch on the main points of interest. Then I will follow it with books on geology, astronomical observations, physics and chemistry, zoological descriptions, and botanical researches."

Caroline's eyes were suddenly wide. "Six books?"

"No," he said gaily. "Six topics. *Seventeen* books. At least. It will take that many volumes to do the job properly."

"And it will also take years to complete such a work."

"Perhaps. Perhaps not." His eyes were glistening chunks of gray in the candlelight. "I really don't know. But this I do know: when I am finished with these books, no one will ever ignore South America again. And no one will forget your brother-in-law."

The girl was quiet for a moment. Then, glancing at him out of the corners of her eyes, she said, "It means a great deal to you, doesn't it? Fame, I mean."

"Doesn't it mean a great deal to everyone?"

"Yes, I suppose it does. But—" Her voice fell away.

"But what?"

She shrugged slightly, unwilling to say the thing that was

on her mind, knowing it would hurt him. Or not touch him at all—which would hurt her. She merely pulled her cloak about her and said, "It doesn't matter, my dear. I'll leave you to your work."

He crossed the room to the door with her. He gave his cheek to her for a goodnight kiss and heard her say, "I'll have breakfast for you and Carlos in my apartment at nine. Do try to sleep a little."

When the door had closed behind her and she stood alone in the dimly lighted hall, she found the words she had wanted to say back there at the littered table. They frightened her as she stood there in the silent morning hours, for they had as their source the second fear she felt for his well-being.

"Enjoy your fame, my dear. You deserve it," she said softly to the closed door. "But, please, don't let it change you."

But by the middle of October she was convinced that he was changing. She attended the first exhibition of his drawings of South America and his plant collections at the Jardin des Plantes. Unlike all the other guests, she gave but a passing glance at the work of many years. With cold fascination, she watched her brother-in-law positively basking in the attentions showered on him. Grandly, he extended rocks from Chimborazo and the Orinoco for awe-struck gentlemen and their cooing ladies to touch. He talked learnedly at a dizzying pace and in a voice that had a curious, sophisticated sing-song quality to it. He laughed all too readily and much too delightedly at the exclamations of the women circling him. With almost foppish grace, he inclined his face over one lacy glove after another.

Caroline felt her face flame with rage and shame. Was this really her beloved brother-in-law, posturing and prattling among the natural enemies of his country? Why, he looked as if he had forgotten the fact that he was a German nobleman, a member of a proud race. He looked for all the world as if he were trying to be a Frenchman!

Her anger drove her to send a letter to Wilhelm at Rome. What should she do, she asked, with a man "who lets himself be carried away by French charm?"

The reply from Italy came swiftly. She must convince Alexander that he should return to Germany, Wilhelm instructed. The adulation of the French was but a passing thing. They were a race of faddists; they went quite mad over anything or anyone unusual, and were just as promptly forgetful. They changed their minds a hundred times a day. Alexander must be made to realize that he would receive true and lasting recognition only in Germany.

Armed with her husband's advice, Caroline approached the explorer—only to see anger write itself over his face. "Germany? Return to Germany? No, thank you, my dear. It's a desert. I plan to remain away from there for the rest of my days."

"But why? What has Germany ever done to you?"

"Not a thing. But that isn't the point. It's a country of cold, unimaginative people. Everything is routine, routine, routine. All is order. Order without imagination. No, Li, it's here in France that I am recognized and appreciated. Napoleon or no Napoleon, Paris is the cultural and scientific center of the world. I have known that all my life. Here I belong. Here I shall stay. And here I shall be happy."

Happy?

In a very few months, he would wonder if that word had any place in his life.

The coronation of Napoleon took place on December 2, 1804. The Pope, as all Paris had known he would, came up from Rome to place the crown of Charlemagne on the dark head of the one-time corporal. The city went wild at the sight of the emperor and his Josephine riding in their magnificent carriage to the reception at the Tuileries.

To that reception went Alexander, dressed in a suit of velvet that had cost him twelve hundred francs. Leaving Caroline for a moment, he was escorted to the reception line to meet Bonaparte.

When at last he stepped before the emperor, he faced a smallish man, his face colorless, his uniform of brilliant blue and white, his decorations many.

The explorer bowed. He saw flat eyes look him up and down. The eyes were unblinking.

Napoleon smiled slightly.

"I understand you collect plants, monsieur."

Alexander considered the question one of mere politeness. He was certain that Napoleon, a recipient of the many reports from the Institut de France, knew of his accomplishments. As politely as the question was put, he answered that he did.

Napoleon's reply was like a slap across the face.

"So does my wife."

The emperor turned swiftly away. A foreigner had been taken care of.

Cold anger came up through Alexander at the insult. But he made an impersonal mask of his face. He smiled at the courtiers and gaudily attired soldiers surrounding their new emperor. Then he himself turned away.

As he turned, he entered a new chapter in his life.

CHAPTER FOURTEEN

Dark Interlude

THE CHAPTER WAS to be a long and dark one. When the explorer entered it Alexander von Humboldt was a man of thirty-five years, straight backed, and with the memory of South America fresh in his mind. When he closed its last page behind him he was still erect, but graying and fifty-nine, and the recollections of the New World were crowded by fresher memories of work, despair, and frustration.

The time of basking in fame was at an end the day he walked out of the Tuileries angered at the insult of the Corsican corporal. In earnest he got down to the task of writing the books he had described with such enthusiasm to Caroline that night in the apartment.

"I need the help of the finest scientists I can find," he told himself, and called in Jean-Baptiste Biot, Achille Valenciennes, Karl Ludwig Willdenow, Georges Cuvier, and Joseph-Louis Gay-Lussac to serve as his collaborators. And he welcomed back to Paris Aimé as his second-in-command on the project.

He threw his arms around the botanist, now stoutish after

a vacation spent devouring the sturdy meals concocted by his brother's wife. "I hope you are rested, my friend. According to my outline, we have seventeen books ahead of us. I estimate that we will be at work on them for seven years."

Seventeen books. Seven years.

Before he was done, he looked on those figures as pathetic shadows of reality. With each page of manuscript completed, the task seemed to grow rather than diminish. Thirty proved to be the number of reality: thirty volumes and thirty years to complete them.

But, when the project was finished, it stood as a giant among scientific literature. It was composed of six parts: the first dealt with the South American journey up to Peru and included the history and geography of the countries visited; the second part focused its attention on the animals of the New World, and the third its people and resources; Part Four had its eyes on both heaven and earth, dealing, in the main, with the astronomical observations that had corrected the geographical positions of hundreds of sites beyond the Atlantic; Parts Five and Six dealt respectively with the geology and plant life of South America. The words that Alexander scribbled on sheet after sheet of manuscript paper finally numbered in the millions; the maps and illustrations, a great many of them hand-colored, reached the number 1,425.

It was a task to stagger the imagination. It served to make the explorer the world's foremost authority on South America and established him, with the sole exception of Napoleon Bonaparte, as the most famous man in the Europe of his time. But it was a task that could not be completed in peace.

In the spring of 1805, with his collaborator and now close

friend, Joseph-Louis Gay-Lussac, Alexander traveled south to visit his brother, Wilhelm, at Rome. Caroline had returned to her husband a month earlier and all was in readiness for her two guests. The reunion was a joyous one. The two brothers—so unlike each other; the one an adventurer; the other a quiet scholar—embraced and, both at the same time, began to pour out the stories of their lives during a separation of six years.

But a shadow soon fell over the visit. Almost immediately, Wilhelm began urging Alexander to visit Germany. "It doesn't matter how you feel about her," he argued. "She is your country. You are one of her most illustrious sons. Not to visit her is an unpardonable snub."

Reluctantly, Alexander admitted the correctness of his brother's arguments and agreed to a visit to Berlin.

"But it will be just a short visit," he warned.

He later remembered that warning with an ironic smile. The "short visit" lasted for more than two years, from November, 1805, to January, 1808. Upon his arrival in Berlin—where he was showered with honors, including a membership in the Academy of Science and the appointment of Court Chamberlain by Friedrich Wilhelm III—he found himself involved with several very clever scientists, among them the astronomer, Jabbo Oltmanns. Despite his feeling that his countrymen were an unimaginative lot, these men were full of ideas that captured his fancy and caused him to postpone again and again his departure for Paris.

With Jabbo Oltmanns, he studied the earth's magnetism, shutting himself up in a small hut made entirely without iron and set down in a garden behind a house in the Leipzigerstrasse. In a year's time, they made more than 6,000 readings of the earth's magnetic behavior in that latitude and accomplished the first uninterrupted recording of a magnetic storm.

Alexander carried on this work under the greatest mental strain, for, while he was trying to keep tired eyes focused on the magnetic needle for hours at a time, the dogs of war were howling at his doorstep. In 1805, Napoleon, still intent on bringing all Europe under his domination, ordered his troops against Germany. Complaining that "Bonaparte makes war with our legs," French legions crossed the Rhine, and the newspapers of Berlin began a long recital of disasters:

"General Mack Surrenders at Ulm."
"Bonaparte Moves on Jena."
"Prussian Army Suffers Crushing Defeat at Jena."
"French Marching on Berlin."

The Prussian King gathered his royal robes about him and fled his capital. The banners of France flowed into the city. Tegel was plundered by occupation troops; paintings and tapestries were torn from the walls; the library was left in ruins; the house was looted from cellar to attic. The only things saved were silver and china buried in the garden before the arrival of the troops.

The horror of war—the spectacle of many men giving their blood and their lives to satisfy the thirsts of one man—drove Alexander to dark depression. Out of this mood came a book called *Views of Nature*. In it—like the poets Keats, Wordsworth, and Shelley—he argued that man will find true happiness only when he unites himself with nature. He addressed it to those tormented souls "who are wearied with the clash of warring nations."

His chance to return to Paris came late in 1807, following the signing of the Treaty of Tilsit, a document that ended the war and put Germany on her knees before Bonaparte. Friedrich Wilhelm III returned to his court at Berlin and Alexander was summoned before him to hear him speak these surprising words:

"Our younger brother, Prince Wilhelm of Prussia, is to journey to France to negotiate with Bonaparte for more lenient peace terms. It is our desire that you accompany His Highness to assist him in these negotiations. You will extend every effort to make his stay in Paris both successful and pleasant."

And so at last, in January of 1808, the explorer found himself once more in the city of the Seine. In the moment of arrival, he told himself, "You will never leave again." The negotiations were completed quickly and Prince Wilhelm returned home. Alexander heaved a sigh of relief.

"I'm finally free of official duties," he told Gay-Lussac. "Now I can get back to work on my books."

And it was about time that he did so. Time was no longer on his side. He was close to forty. The first flecks of gray were showing in his hair. The lines of age were deepening about his mouth. If he didn't finish his South American writings soon, he would find himself too old for further explorations.

But he still could not work in peace. The years were filled with worry and sorrow and war. The costs of publication were proving so tremendous that Humboldt felt it only right that he help with its financing. Though a noble gesture, it came close to breaking him financially and physically. While he tried to pour his millions of words onto his manuscript paper, he was plagued by pyramiding bills. Illustrators, printers, and engravers dunned him for their money. His desire for perfection contributed to the chaos. If he didn't like the look of an illustration in copperplate, he promptly destroyed it and then had to bear the expense of having it redone. The burden became so great that he was forced to take a small room at the École Polytechnique and once wrote a friend that "although I have lost everything, I fancy that I shall be able to enjoy independence on forty sous a day."

Carlos Montúfar had returned home to Ecuador in 1809; a year later, word came back to Alexander that the young nobleman had been executed at the end of an unsuccessful rebellion against the Spanish authorities. Alexander cast his pen aside. He covered his face with his hands. How could he possibly write while he pictured that young body crumpled in the dust and its eager heart burning in the plaza at Quito?

On top of these difficulties, Aimé did not turn out to be an able right hand. The Frenchman was a genius when working in the field, but he was lost at a desk, impatient and careless with paper work. One of Alexander's most discouraging moments in all the years of writing came the day the botanist burst into the tiny apartment and cried:

"Alex, I've just received the most wonderful news! The Empress Josephine has employed me to attend her gardens at Malmaison."

Alexander heard the words coldly. A small knot of pain formed itself somewhere behind his eyes. He laid his pen aside carefully. Trying to quell the anger rising slowly within him, he spoke patiently, "But, Aimé, you can't accept. You're needed here. There's so much to be done. What will happen to the books?"

Aimé met his friend's white, tired face with a smile. He came around the desk and placed his hands on Alexander's shoulders. "Nothing will happen to the books, Alex. I can carry on my part of the work at Malmaison as well as I can here. It's not at the other end of the world, you know."

Alexander shook his head. The sense of frustration he felt was a choking thing. "That's easier said than done, Aimé, and you know it." There was a note of humble pleading in his voice that the aristocrat in him despised.

He watched the smile on Aimé's face dissolve. "Alex, I can't remain here. This working indoors is driving me mad. All the words and all the pictures—" he gestured disgustedly at the papers littering the desk—"I've grown to hate them. I'm just not the man for this sort of work. I've got to get outdoors again, among plants and flowers."

The explorer surrendered, just as he had known he would from the very first moment of the conversation. "All right, Aimé. I can't stop you. You know what is best for yourself."

"It is for the best all around," the Frenchman insisted. "I promise you, I'll keep abreast of the work."

But it was *not* for the best and Alexander knew it as soon as the door had closed behind his friend. Immediately upon the botanist's departure, the flow of pages from his hand began to dwindle. The situation worsened steadily through the months until the explorer was forced to write him in desperation, "You do not send me a line on your botany. I beg and beseech you to hold out until the work is completed. . . . Do pray send us some manuscript. . . . The public is under the impression that you have lost all interest in science. . . . I embrace you affectionately, and in the course of a month I shall know whether you still love me sufficiently to gratify my wishes."

It was the most difficult letter he had ever had to write in his life. Looking at it, he felt as if the faithful, tireless Aimé of the Orinoco had died and an inadequate stranger had taken his name and face.

Not all the moments of those dark years were depressing. There was, for instance, the moment in late 1804 when the explorer faced the lean young scientist, Jean-Baptiste Biot, across a map of the world spread out on a table and said, "I have been putting on this map all my recordings of the earth's magnetic intensity in South America. I can now see complete a pattern I suspected all the while the recordings were being made. Look."

He touched the blue of northern Europe. The map was covered with tiny lines, each of them bearing a number.

"See how the readings that others have taken up here in the lands close to the north magnetic pole reveal a great magnetic intensity in the earth." His hand jumped down to South America. "But look what I found. As I moved south over the New World, the magnetic intensity decreased little by little until it was at its lowest point here at the magnetic equator."

His finger traveled south of that imaginary line. "And now see how the magnetic intensity again increases as you move toward the south magnetic pole."

Biot inclined his sharp features over the map. "I see. There, too, are points here where the magnetic intensity is greater than at other spots within the same general area."

"That is due to the magnetism in certain geological formations," Alexander explained. "But, in the main, the intensity decreases as you move away from the poles. It's a definite pattern. You can't miss it."

And so was stated for the first time a new scientific law—the law of declining magnetic intensity between the poles. The law was stated a week later before the Institut de France, and science came to know that another secret of the earth's always mysterious behavior had been uncovered.

At about the same time, Alexander met and became friendly with the thirty-one-year-old Venezuelan, Simón Bolívar. The friendship led to two surprises for the explorer. First, upon his return to South America, Bolívar took command of a series of revolutions that ultimately resulted in the independence from Spain of the countries of Venezuela, Ecuador, Panama, Peru, Colombia, and Bolivia.

The second surprise came some years later when he heard

that, at the height of his power, Bolívar had said, "Some years ago I had the honor of cultivating the friendship of Baron de Humboldt, whose learning has done America more good than all the conquerors."

"Strange," the explorer thought, "that the fight for freedom that I sensed for so long was coming to South America should finally be brought to pass by a man of my acquaintance." Though he never took seriously the claim of many that he inspired Bolívar to the "Second American Revolution," he was pleased always to remember that the Venezuelan had credited him with having prompted him, Bolívar, to a deeper study of the countries he subsequently led to independence.

Another great moment came for the explorer in 1817 when the many temperature recordings made in South America enabled him to draw lines connecting areas of similar climates in the world. He called them, *isothermal lines*. With them, he had devised a simple technique for comparing climatic conditions of various countries. They were to be put to great use in later years in the science of climatology and the work of weather forecasting.

Meanwhile the dogs of war had set up their chilling baying again. Napoleon marched into Russia and collided with defeat. French troops fell back across Germany. Their eyes widened with horror as, making a stand at Leipzig, they saw Mongolians, Russians, Austrians, and, by the thousands, German students, merchants, poets, scholars, and shopkeepers charge their lines, their bayonets eager to rip away all the insults of past years. The legions of Bonaparte fled before this onslaught and their emperor fled with them.

The entire time Napoleon was retreating across Germany, Alexander remained in Paris. His conscience cried that he should hurry across the Rhine to play his small part in stamping out the disease that was the Corsican corporal.

Wilhelm had abandoned Rome and was there now, as was his son Theodor.

"The world will call me a coward, perhaps even a traitor," he told Gay-Lussac in the small apartment they shared at the École Polytechnique. "But I can't go. I can't help myself. I *must* stay here. I must finish my work." His eyes, full of pleading for understanding, sought out Gay-Lussac's. "Is not the work I am doing—the giving of knowledge to the world—more important than war?"

Gay-Lussac nodded slowly, thoughtfully. "With all my heart, I believe it is. But do the people? And does your king? You must be ready to suffer at their hands."

He was. Quite ready. For the work was now an obsession with him. It had all but broken him financially. It had created a rift between the beloved Aimé and himself. It had chained him to a desk when he wanted to go wandering over distant lands. But it was valuable work. It had to be finished at all cost. Europe must know of the wonders far across the Atlantic. Science must know of all that he had found.

Into Paris swept Napoleon and his battered troops. Close upon their heels came the victorious armies of Germany, Russia, and Austria, their cannon rattling over French roads, their bayonets knifing aside the green youths Bonaparte was forced to send out against them. Bonaparte, watching his Senate abandon him, abdicated at Fountainebleu on April 14, 1814, and was thrust along the humiliating path that would finally lead to the stern sheets of a small boat sailing for Elba.

Now the conquering monarchs closed on Paris in their splendid coaches. Upon their arrival, Alexander was summoned into the presence of Friedrich Wilhelm III. He steeled himself for the interview. He was ready for the suffering that Gay-Lussac had mentioned. He was ready to have the charge, "coward and traitor" flung into his face.

But—wonder of wonders—the German monarch greeted him cordially. Yes, Baron von Humboldt had been thoughtless. And selfish. And unpatriotic. But Friedrich was willing to forgive and forget. Alexander was again to join his court. He could remain in Paris, serving his king from a distance.

Friedrich's attitude left the explorer weak with astonishment. But it did not surprise wise Parisians in the least. "Any fool can see that this Humboldt is so famous that even royalty won't step on his toes," they said. "And look at poor Friedrich. He's an oaf, really, as stupid as a man can be and still be able to find his way home. What was it Boney used to call him? A tailor, wasn't it? Because he seemed interested in nothing but designing pretty uniforms for his soldiers. Yes, he's stupid, all right, but just smart enough to realize that Humboldt's genius can be of service to him."

Alexander was to remain in Paris for another thirteen years and that genius, which the French people had so easily recognized in him, was to serve Friedrich on numerous occasions. In 1814, he accompanied the monarch on a journey to London; 1817 saw him with Friedrich at the Congress of Aix-la-Chapelle; 1822 at the Congress of Verona and on visits to Rome and Naples.

Finally, on firm orders from the King of Prussia, he left Paris behind him and, at the age of fifty-seven, settled permanently in a Berlin apartment in May, 1827.

For many years Humboldt's thoughts were devoted to a tragedy that had nothing to do with his king.

In 1816, Aimé Bonpland departed from Europe, bound for a second exploration of South America.

He was given a most flattering reception at Buenos Aires and was appointed professor of natural history. Fortune smiled on him until 1820, when he ventured on a surveying trip into an area over which there was dispute between Paraguay and Argentina. Dr. José Francia, dictator of Paraguay, suspecting him of being a spy, ordered him to be taken prisoner. On the night of December 3, 1821, his camp was attacked by a troop of cavalry. His servants were killed and he himself was wounded in the head, placed in chains, and transported to Paraguay where he was thrust into prison.

The thought of his friend caged in a jail cell was too much for Alexander. Such a life—even for a short period—would kill the Bonpland who required the freedom of the outdoors to survive. Memories of their South American adventures and of their close friendship drove from mind his disappointment over Aimé's desertion of the work on the books. The explorer threw all his efforts into a campaign for the botanist's release, writing letters to the officials of the Paraguayan government, sending a personal representative to Francia, and even appealing to the British Prime Minister, Canning, for help.

All this effort was in vain. Bonpland, made to serve as a doctor and supervisor of agricultural affairs at one of Francia's garrisons, was held captive for nine years, finally being released in 1830. By that time, he was broken in health and in spirit. He refused to return to Europe, choosing instead the life of a hermit in the wilds of Brazil. The life that had started so gloriously beside Alexander on the day the *Pizarro* sailed out of La Coruña now faded into obscurity. Within twenty years, his name was all but forgotten in Europe.

During the years 1827 to 1829, Alexander might well have wished that he, too, had chosen the life of a hermit.

His days were crowded to the bursting point with court duties. He instructed his monarch's family in the latest scientific and cultural advancements. He was called upon night after night to serve as a pleasant, witty ornament at

Friedrich's dinners and banquets. He was given the task of caring for the king's correspondence, a responsibility that involved the writing of close to 2,000 letters a year. The writing of his South American books was limited to the darkest hours of the night.

And what of his desire to travel again? The desire still flamed within him, with the intensity of the years of long ago, but the opportunity to take to the road once more always seemed just beyond the reach of his aging fingers. He had planned many expeditions, but not one of them had advanced beyond the paper stage. Twice—in 1811 and 1818—he had been offered the chance to explore Asia; twice the opportunity had evaporated before his eyes. And a plan that he had formulated to visit India and Tibet had been destroyed by the British government when they had refused to grant him visas to those countries.

By 1829, at the age of fifty-nine, he was certain that he was doomed to a life without travel; doomed to the dull existence of teacher to and letter writer for a stupid king.

Then, without advance warning, a letter arrived from Russia.

CHAPTER FIFTEEN

Russia

THE LETTER WAS FROM Count Georg Cancrin, the Russian Minister of Finance.

It placed a very simple question before the explorer: would Baron von Humboldt find interesting the idea of traveling through Russia and studying that country's natural resources?

The letter had been born some weeks earlier at St. Petersburg during a meeting between Tsar Nicholas I and Cancrin. Both were concerned over the fact that their nation, physically a giant, played the role of a dwarf in world affairs. Russia had kept too much to herself in centuries past. It was time that she step forward and assume a position of influence befitting her size.

But, before she could seriously hope to take such a step, she must convince the rest of the world of the wealth of her resources. It was then that Cancrin voiced the idea that led to the writing of the letter. Would not it be wise to invite Baron von Humboldt, the leading explorer of the day, to investigate Russia's resources? The publication of his findings would create a new respect in Europe for a nation intent on making her bid for international prominence.

Nicholas agreed to the soundness of the plan. The letter was composed and dispatched. Now the two men had only to wait for a reply from the explorer. Would he show interest in such a venture at his age?

Had they known the mind of their man, they would not have concerned themselves for a moment over his answer.

He was most certainly interested.

The Russians had made him young again.

On April 12, 1829, at the end of seventeen months of preparation, a fifty-nine-year-old Alexander sat very erect in the coach bound for the Russian border. He breathed deeply—freely, it seemed to him, for the first time in years—as he listened to the clatter of the horses' hoofs over the frozen road and watched the countryside of northern Germany sweep up to him through swirling snowflakes and then fall away behind his shoulder. The wind burned his face with an icy fire.

Directly across from him sat the two scientists who were to share in his new adventures—Professor Christian Gottfried Ehrenberg, who had accomplished such splendid studies on the microscopic life in lakes, and the brilliant young mineralogist, Gustav Rose. As he had so often in the past weeks, Alexander congratulated himself on the choice of these companions. Ehrenberg would investigate the life in and the chemical content of the waters of the Caspian Sea; Rose would collect minerals, leaving the explorer himself free to concentrate on magnetic readings and a survey of Russia's natural resources. In a second carriage, the thunder of which he could discern above the rattle and scrape of his own coach, the faithful and fussy Karl Seifert, his servant of the past two years, rode amidst piles of luggage and scientific gear.

He grinned at the memory of how Seifert had fretted over him at the beginning of the journey this morning. He murmured to himself, "He's an old woman."

The young Rose, his face blue with the cold and his hands stuffed into the pockets of a heavy greatcoat, lifted his head. "What was that, sir?"

"I was just thinking what an old woman Seifert is. Did you notice how I had to have a cup of strong coffee before we left and how I had to have this infernal blanket wrapped about my legs? Sometimes I agree with what many people say: that he—not I—is the master of my house."

It was Ehrenberg's turn to stir. His hat was pulled down over the bridge of his nose—a nose of shining purple. His ears were covered with muffs and a woolen scarf came up over his chin. He glowered at the open window. "He would die if he knew you had raised those shades."

"How else can we see the countryside?" the explorer countered, thinking: and what miserable countryside it is; here we are in the middle of April, and it looks like the dead of winter. "Don't let the cold bother you. It was far worse than this in the Andes and I was never healthier."

Ehrenberg, shivering, shot another glance at the window. Then he ventured a comment that Rose, although agreeing with it in secret, would not have dared to make because of his youth. "But, Baron, that was twenty-five years ago. You have grown older since then, you know."

Alexander waved impatiently. "Bah! Old, am I? Is that what you think? Well, you'll find out I am quite capable of standing up to anything this journey has to offer. You will see."

And they did see, long before the Russian border was reached. Wind and snow beat at them constantly. At the

Vistula River they descended from the carriage in a raging blizzard and stamped their feet and swung their arms while the coaches, their teams snorting with fright, were taken aboard flat barges and lashed down. The crossing to the opposite shore was like a scene from a nightmare. The wind set the barges to swinging badly. Visibility was limited to just a few feet by the falling snow. Men with pikes were stationed along the rails. Their job was to prevent floating ice from ramming into the vessel.

Alexander seemed in his element. He strode along the length of the barge, his hands stuffed in the pockets of his brown greatcoat. Once, the ever-watchful Karl Seifert grabbed his elbow as he leaned far out over the rail to watch a giant chunk of ice being pushed away.

He shook himself free of the servant's grasp. "Don't be a fool, Karl! I won't fall in."

Immediately he saw the hurt in the man's eyes. Seifert said in an injured tone, "I was only trying to be of service to you."

Alexander nodded an apology, then drew Seifert to him. "You can do me a real service if you wish." He winked so broadly that snow came off his eyebrow. He pointed to the carriage in which Ehrenberg and Rose were huddled, blowing furiously into their gloved hands. "Simply ask Professor Ehrenberg who is the old lady now."

Seifert showed just the correct amount of shock and impatience. "As you desire, Baron," he said and retired with as much dignity as a pitching deck and a high wind would allow.

The river was but an introduction to the difficulties ahead. Beyond the town of Königsberg, the travelers were, in Alexander's words, "surrounded by all the horrors of winter; and saw nothing but snow and ice as far as the eye can reach." As for the roads, they were "so much washed away that the front wheels become buried in the mud, and travelers have to provide themselves with planks, that, with extra horses and the manual labor of the peasantry, the carriages may be helped over the deepest ruts."

However, the journey did have its moments of ease. The crossing of the Russian border was one of them. "Red tape," Alexander growled as the carriage, coated with mud and splashed with snow, rattled up to the border station. "Russia is one of the most difficult countries in the world to enter. We'll very likely be held up here for hours." This was not the case. Passports were checked swiftly, the customary investigation of luggage waived, and the coaches were sent on their way in a matter of minutes.

"I must thank Cancrin when I see him," Alexander said. "He did his work well. I'll wager those fellows back there were told months ago to expect our arrival."

The carriages jolted northward. The planks were brought out daily to see them across giant mudholes. Once, the travelers had to dig the lead coach out of a snowdrift with their bare hands. Before St. Petersburg was sighted they had been ferried across rivers seventeen times.

St. Petersburg, then the capital of Russia, was reached on May 1, 1829. The carriages, now fit only for the junk yard, limped up to the residence of Lieutenant General von Schöler, the Prussian Ambassador, and the bone weary travelers stepped forth to be caught up in a swirl of welcoming ceremonies.

At first, the hospitality of the Russians overwhelmed Alexander. He was greeted by government officials. A collection of maps from the government printing press was presented to him. He was conducted on a tour of this city on the Neva. Three carriages, each costing twelve hundred thalers, were brought forth to replace the two delapidated veterans of the journey up from Germany. A courier and a cook were provided for the remainder of the Russian exploration.

Of those first days in St. Petersburg, the explorer wrote, "I am surrounded by excitement wherever I go, and it would be impossible to be treated with greater distinction or more generous hospitality. I have dined nearly every day with the Imperial Family in their strictest privacy—covers being laid for four—and I have spent the evenings with the Empress in the most delightful freedom from constraint. The heir apparent also entertained me to dinner, 'in order that he may remember me in time to come.' The young prince has been told to ask for my portrait. . . ."

But very soon all the attention began to wear on Alexander. On May 20, the travelers moved on to Moscow for a fortnight's stay and a note of impatience began to appear in his writings. "We are continually the objects of attention with the police, government officials, Cossacks, and guards of honor. Unfortunately, we are scarcely a moment alone; we cannot take a step without being led by the arm like an invalid."

The route out of Moscow, which was to cut a sawtooth pattern eastward to the borders of Chinese Tatary, led through the towns of Mourom and Nijnii-Novgorod (now named Gorki) and southeast along the Volga river to Kazan.

Spring was now on the land. The Volga was at floodtide. The villages and the surrounding land, beginning to flower with the coming of warm weather, murmured a siren song for Alexander. But he had little or no time to enjoy them. Tsar Nicholas had sent orders ahead that the distinguished tourists were to be greeted with the honors befitting a senator or a general. Those instructions led to one maddening celebration after another.

At one stop, he was presented with a sword from mining officials and then—hating any and all forms of music—he grimly had to paint a smile on his face and courageously hold it there while a chorus of Tatar sultanas serenaded him. And at another town the explorer was forced to dance a quadrille.

The halts at military garrisons were almost as trying. There would always be waiting for the carriages crowds of Cossacks, soldiers of the line, Baschkirians, Tatars, and Russians, all of them costumed in their heavy, colorful uniforms. At some posts Alexander was obliged to listen attentively and politely while the commanding officer, following military custom, reported to him on the condition of local troops.

"It's infuriating," he complained to Ehrenberg and Rose. "We're seeing only what they want us to see. Oh, I know they're being kind, but we're wasting our time unless we can achieve some freedom of movement."

"I wouldn't say it's been a complete waste," Ehrenberg said blandly, prodding Rose's elbow gently. "At least, Baron, you've learned to dance the quadrille."

The travelers finally got down to work when they entered the Ural, that vast mountain chain that rises to a height of 4,600 feet and, running due north and south, drops from the Arctic Ocean to the Caspian Sea. This area, one of the richest in the world in natural resources, was the one that Tsar Nicholas particularly wanted his visitors to study. And study it they did.

In mid-June, far east of the city of Kazan, they crossed the geographic boundary separating Europe from Asia, and visited laboratories for the cutting of topaz, beryl, and amethyst. The same month saw them taking notes on the iron furnaces of Nijnii-Issetek and the gold fields of Schabrowski.

Arriving at Iekaterinburg, they swung north for an inspection of the platinum fields in the area of Nijnii-Tagilsk (Tagil). One of the fields was owned by a Prince Demidov and it had made such a wealthy man of him that Ehrenberg observed:

"I've always wanted to see someone living in true Oriental splendor. Well, now I've seen him."

To which Alexander replied, "How else could he possibly live? This area yields as much ore as that of Choco in South America."

Back down to Iekaterinburg they went and then eastward, with each day of July revealing to them more and more of the immense wealth of the country. They reached Tobolsk, the city on the banks of the Irtysch river, and cut southeast across the steppes of Barabinsk, alive with swarms of stinging insects, to visit the silver mines of the Snake and Altai mountains.

Not only did Alexander see natural resources that were already being worked, but he guessed the presence of a resource that had remained concealed from Russian eyes for centuries. In the Ural Mountains he sighted geological formations greatly similar to some in Brazil where diamonds had been found and this similarity prompted him to write Cancrin, "The Ural Mountains are a true El Dorado. . . . I am confident . . . that under your administration diamonds will be found in the gold and platinum washings of the Ural. . . ."

Actually, the discovery came sooner than he had expected —and at hands other than his. Along the eastward route, he had encountered an old friend, Count Polier, who owned land in the Ural. His suspicion of the precious stones in the area drove the Count to go in search of them on his own estate. Upon Alexander's return to St. Petersburg, he learned that Polier's quest had been successful. His workers had unearthed, first, a diamond of one and one-half carats, and had then proceeded to find larger stones. At St. Petersburg, Alexander received a package containing a diamond from the grateful Count, plus a note crediting the explorer with being the true discoverer of the precious stones in Russia.

August saw the carriages speeding toward the Chinese border at such a rate that Alexander wrote to his brother, "One travels—or rather flees—across these monotonous grasslands as over an ocean, sailing on land as it were, in which we covered 140 miles in twenty-four hours. We suffered greatly from heat, dust, and yellow mosquitoes. . . ."

They reached the small fortress of Ust-Kamenogorsk on August 18. This was as far east as they were to go. They had reached the border of China. Alexander obtained permission to cross the frontier and paid a brief visit to the Mongolian station at Baty. A tiny wave of sadness came up through him. He was standing at the gate of one of the most fascinating lands in the world, a vast country that had captured the fancy of every explorer since the beginning of time. All his life he had longed to roam over that land stretching away to and then beyond the distant, purple mountains. But he knew it was too late in life for him to plan such a venture. China would have to be left to others.

Now, following a southerly route, the travelers swung westward for the return to St. Petersburg. They passed through Omsk, pausing to investigate the gold fields of Miask where they heard an official say, "Three nuggets such as I have never seen before were found here just inches below the surface. Two of them weighed fifteen pounds. The third came to twenty-three pounds."

Their next main stop was at the beautiful jasper quarries near Orsk. Then, in October, they were on the shores of the Caspian Sea.

"Now I come into my own," Ehrenberg announced.

An aged steamboat was rented and he spent the days happily collecting samples of water and bringing up various fish to the deck. He tested the water for chemical content and from it obtained excellent data on the microbial life present in fresh water. The information obtained and the fish caught would be of great value to Georges Cuvier and Achille Valenciennes in their current study of the fish of the world.

The last lap of their journey was at hand. They shot northward, first to Moscow, and then to St. Petersburg. In both cities, they were welcomed like returning heroes. At Moscow, Alexander was awarded the Order of St. Anne of the first class, Ehrenberg and Rose receiving the same decoration, but of the second class. At a reception at the Scientific Society, a speaker referred to him as "Humboldt, Prométhée de nos jours"—Prometheus of our time. At St. Petersburg, he received a sable cloak worth 5,000 rubles and, in his own words, "a vase as beautiful as any in the palace, standing, with pedestal included, seven feet high, worth from 35,000 to 40,000 rubles."

And, finally, Tsar Nicholas took his hand and said, "Your sojourn in Russia has been the cause of immense progress in my country; you spread a life-giving influence wherever you go." So far as the Tsar was concerned, Alexander had done his work well. All the crates of minerals he was taking back to Germany and all the writings he was to publish of his journey would leave no one in doubt of Russia's wealth, a wealth that would enable her to play a greater role in world affairs.

On December 15th, the travelers put St. Petersburg behind them and started for the German border. Alexander sat quietly, immersed in his own thoughts, paying no attention to the fast falling snow. Unlike the Tsar, he was disappointed in the Russian venture—from one standpoint, at least. The politeness and enthusiasm of the Russians had actually gotten in the way of his work; and the speed with which the journey had to be made so that it would be finished ahead of the Asian winter had reduced his views of

Russia to fleeting glimpses. In the space of twenty-five weeks, he had traveled a total of 9,614 miles. He had visited 658 post stations and the incredible number of 12,000 horses had been used on the journey. He had made fifty-three river crossings, twelve of the Volga, eight of the Irtysch, and two of Obi. By the time he reached his starting point, Berlin, he gauged he would have traveled 11,505 miles. He had crammed into six months almost as much travel as he had into four years in the New World.

Yet there was a bright side to the picture. After he had received the order of St. Anne at Moscow, he had described his many magnetic recordings made throughout the trip and he had urged the officials present to press for the establishment of a line of magnetic and meteorological stations across the face of northern Asia for the purpose of studying the earth's magnetic behavior. Who could tell where such an enterprise would lead?

He would one day know that his plea, resulting in the stations he requested, would lead to the establishment of the International Union for Magnetic Studies. He would go down in history as a highly influential pioneer in the bringing into being of the world's first co-operative scientific society.

As he sat there in the coach, he knew that the Russian adventure had done something strange to—or for—him. It seemed to him as if, after all the long years since Tegel, he had finally quenched the flames of travel in his being. Surprisingly, in the midst of all the hurry and all the celebrations, he had found time to think of the future and, just as surprising, he had found that exploration had no place in that future. Foremost in his mind and looming as fascinating as travel had once seemed to him, was a vast project that had been growing in his imagination for a long while. That it would tie him to a desk and make a hermit of him for the rest of his days bothered him not in the least.

He knew he must now complete his South American books and his writings on Russia as quickly as was humanly possible. For, after those tasks were out of the way, he was going to try to compress the entire universe between the covers of a book.

CHAPTER SIXTEEN

Immortality

THE YEAR 1843 saw the end of Alexander's writings on the New World and Asia. By that time, he was the author of more than forty books—including the original thirty scientific works he had planned on South America, seven volumes of popular narrative on his travels with Aimé Bonpland, and three volumes on the Russian adventure published under the general title, *Asie Centrale, recherches sur les chaînes des montagnes et la climatologie comparée.*

Now the explorer, white-haired and seventy-four, turned his full attention to the grand project he had envisioned during the coach trip from St. Petersburg.

And what an ambitious project it was! He had been doing some work on it already and the thought of what he was trying to do often staggered him and caused him to refer to the project as a "mad notion." As he once wrote, he was going to try to depict in a "graphic and attractive manner the whole of the physical aspect of the universe in one work, which is to include all that is known of celestial and terrestial phenomena, from the nature of a nebula down to the geography of the mosses clinging to a granite rock."

But, though the work staggered him, it also delighted him. It would serve for all time to come as a flashing, brilliant crown for his cherished theory of the harmony in nature. The Andes had revealed to him the beauty of the harmony rising in a series of changing plant forms from steaming jungles to snowy peaks. Tenerife, Cotopaxi, Jorullo, and all the other lava cones he had scaled had shown him the harmony existing between volcanoes and vast underground fissures. The Incas and the Aztecs and the Mayans, with their clues to a connection with ancient Oriental civilizations, had indicated a flow of the harmony among the peoples of the earth. Now he would attempt to show the harmony—the basic unity—in *all* natural phenomena. "And," he promised himself, "with every grand and important idea must be given the facts upon which it rests."

And why was he driven to attempt such a work at his age and while burdened with the many responsibilities of his position as Privy Councilor to the new German king, Friedrich Wilhelm IV? The answer was simple.

The world was entering the age of science. It was going to be an age that might well break man; in an era of one bewildering discovery after another, man might lose sight of his position in and value to the world; he might easily become an unthinking cog in the machinery of industry; or he might come to view science as solely a means of contributing to his comfort and wealth, thereby casting away much of his human dignity. But if he could be helped to understand the basic principles on which the sprawling universe rested, then he would be able to understand his own position in that universe. He would be able to build a happy, balanced, and useful life for himself.

A work that could accomplish that was well worth writing, no matter if you had to slave at it until the far reaches of the night when your aging body was crying for rest; no matter how exhausted you were after long days spent advising your monarch and writing letters for him; no matter how many times you were interrupted by people who came from over the world to visit you.

To the project that was finally to fill five volumes he gave the title, *Cosmos*.

He began with what he called a "survey of nature." Book One dealt first with the realm of outer space, concentrating on the planets and cosmic nebulae, and then turned earthward for a description of the atmospheric and geologic forces that exert such a great influence on the lives of human beings, plants, and animals.

Book Two told of the spell of inspiration and mystery that nature has cast over man since the beginning of time. In it, Alexander explained how artists through the ages have drawn inspiration from natural objects and how the earliest peoples assigned human feelings to plants and animals, and how they found deities in such natural forces as earthquakes, fire, storms, and the sun.

The remaining three volumes of the work constituted a survey of scientific knowledge up to Alexander's time. Book Three told the story of astronomy. It began with Aristotle and his concept of unified energies producing a world order. It concluded with the classification of the stars by Sir John Herschel.

Volume Four turned again to the earth for a survey of the world's physical properties. It contained all that the explorer had learned of the earth's magnetism and, in addition, provided a statistical history of the world's major earthquakes and volcanic eruptions.

Book Five was to deal with geology. . . .

The day was April 19, 1859.

The man who sat at the writing desk was eighty-nine years of age. His hair was snow-white and thinning just above his forehead. There were deep lines at the corners of his mouth and cutting outward beneath his cheeks from his nostrils. His skin was drawn tightly over his bones and lips that had once been inclined to fullness were now thin and sunken.

He sat hunched over a sheet of paper, a quill pen in his hand. All the morning he had been writing swiftly in that illegible, uphill hand of his, lifting the pen from the page only long enough to dip it in an inkwell. There were three sounds in the room: the crackle of the fire in the grate off to his left, the hurried scratching of the pen, and his labored, aged breathing.

Suddenly one of the three sounds was no longer heard. The pen, coming to the end of a paragraph, halted. Alexander sat back in the chair, staring vacantly at the page. He had felt fear but a few times in his life: the day he had come face-to-face with the jaguar on the Apure, the night Aimé had ventured so close to death at Angostura, and the moments off Cartagena when the sloop had lay on her beam ends, ready to go under. Now he knew he was feeling fear again, a strange, quiet fear that had come from nowhere while the slanting words were rushing on to the page. Like a shadow, it had passed before his eyes and had left him with the icy knowledge that the time remaining to him in life was no longer an unknown quantity. It was but a matter of days. It was time to put his affairs in order.

Ordinarily, he had no patience with premonitions. All men contemplated death at various times in their lives, and it seemed that the older they got the more often they thought of it. It was a very natural thing to do. But there had been something a little beyond the natural in the knowledge left by that shadow. There was something very final about it and he could not ignore it.

And so, quietly and resignedly, as if he had no will to do otherwise, he began to gather all his footnotes and references for the pages he had thus far written on Volume Five of *Cosmos*. He worked slowly, concentrating on his physical actions so that the shadow would not be given the chance to steal across his vision again. When he was finished, he placed notes and manuscript in an envelope. Then he rang for Seifert.

The servant, now in his late fifties and as stocky and square-faced as ever, entered the room.

Alexander held the envelope out to him. "I want you to take this to Cotta."

Seifert weighed the manuscript in his hand. There were less pages here than the explorer usually dispatched to the publisher.

"Is this all?"

Alexander nodded. "Yes. I'm afraid that is all."

He regretted immediately not the words but his tone. He had not meant to allow such resignation and finality to enter his voice. He saw Seifert eye him sharply.

"Are you all right, Baron?"

"Yes, of course." Now there was testiness in his voice. He disliked himself for behaving like an old fool. "I am fine."

"You're certain?"

"Yes."

Seifert nodded, not at all satisfied. He gave his employer another searching look and then moved to the door. At the threshold he paused and studied Alexander again. The explorer thought briefly that he looked like an old, square-faced hen fretting over a delicate, helpless chick.

"I'll be back soon," Seifert said. "Then I'll fix tea. You'd better rest."

"Stop worrying about me," Alexander said. "I am quite capable of taking care of myself, you know."

"Yes, I know," Seifert said patiently. "Nevertheless, you'd best do as I say. Rest a little while."

The servant closed the door behind himself, very slowly and, it seemed to Alexander, very reluctantly. He fully expected to see the square face pop back into the room again for a last troubled glance at him. Instead, he heard beyond the door Seifert's customary huffing and puffing as he struggled into a topcoat. His ears followed the servant out of the apartment, down the stairs, out the front door, and along the sidewalk; and he thought: he knows. Just as I know, he knows.

He wondered idly what Seifert was going to do without him. The German and his wife had built their lives about him for more than twenty years now. People laughed a great deal at the unsmiling Karl, saying behind his back that he ruled the Humboldt house. In the eyes of Berlin, he was a tyrant. Perhaps he was; he decided when his master should rest; he attended to the payment of bills; he met all visitors and determined whether or not they should interrupt his employer at work. Well, if he was a tyrant, he was a good one, Alexander told himself, a valuable one. Seifert had helped to make it possible for him to come as far with *Cosmos* as he had. He was going to dislike leaving him behind.

There were many things he was going to dislike leaving behind. He looked about the room. The tables and chairs and even the old green sofa were lost beneath stacks of books and manuscripts and portfolios of drawings. Peering silently and unblinkingly at him from all sides were stuffed birds and small animals. Along all the walls were shelves filled with mineral and plant specimens. The walls themselves were completely hidden behind large maps and paintings of animals and flowers and jungles. In this and the sitting room beyond was his whole life.

But he could not complain about leaving these rooms, about leaving life behind him. He had been given more years than most of the men of his time had been granted, so many years indeed that sometimes he felt quite alone in the world. Thomas Jefferson was gone. Simón Bolívar. His brother Wilhelm and the beautiful, gentle Caroline. Friedrich Wilhelm III. Napoleon Bonaparte. Horatio Nelson, Carlos Montúfar. Charles Baudin, Aimé Bonpland.

At the thought of that last name, his eyes misted over. He shook himself impatiently. This was one of the problems of old age; he had never been one for tears, but of late the mist had developed the habit of coming upon him most unexpectedly.

And, he continued thinking, he could not complain about the life he had been given. It had been a life that had seen the rise and fall of the modern world's most remarkable dictator, the founding in North America of a new nation dedicated to liberty, the death of Spanish colonial rule in South America, and the birth of the "age of science." And it had been a life that had been fortunate enough to cross the lives of some of the greatest men of the period in which it had been lived—Goethe, Mutis, Jefferson, Madison, Bonaparte, Cuvier, Biot, and Bolívar. And it had been a life that had sewn a place of importance for itself in the tapestry of history.

It had been a life full of good days, a life of ambitions realized, a life of accomplishments. What more could any man ask for? The explorer had turned in his chair and, with his big chin supported in an ink stained hand, he stared into the fire. It was warm against his face and the memories of some of the accomplishments were warm in his mind.

—Germany's first training school for miners at the little village of Steben.

—The determination of the connection between the Orinoco and Amazon river systems, a feat of great significance to the economic and social development of eastern South America.

—The correction of the geographical position of so many cities and localities in the New World, corrections that were serving as the basis for all the modern maps of South America.

—The wonderful theory of the harmony in nature that was leading to many advancements in agriculture and the sciences of botany and geology; and the theory of the importance of studying all natural phenomena in their associations with one another, which was earning him a place among the fathers of modern geography.

—The Chimborazo climb that had seen him reach a higher point on earth than any man before him and that had prepared the way for the first explorations of the Andes and the Himalayas.

—The writings on the Incas and Aztecs and Mayans that awakened Europe to an understanding of the true worth of all South American Indians and that aroused anthropologists and archaeologists to study these peoples and to search for a possible ancient link between the east and west.

—The thousands of magnetic readings that had led to the recognition of the law of declining magnetic intensity between the poles and the establishment of the International Union for Magnetic Studies, the first organization in the world in which the scientific brains of various nations were pooled for a common cause.

—The explanation to the field of geology that volcanoes extend across the face of the earth linearly and that they are linked with vast underground fissures.

—All the plants and minerals and animals collected, and all the writing, that had alerted the world to the wonders of South America and that had established Humboldt as the foremost authority of his age on that vast land.

—The discovery of diamonds in the Ural Mountains.

—And, finally, the attempt in *Cosmos* to portray in writing for mankind the entire physical universe.

Such work, he reflected, had brought him honors sufficient to satisfy any man. In addition to decorations received and the accolade "King of Science," bestowed on him by many of his calling, he had had many geographical features named after him, including:

—Humboldt Counties in California, Iowa, and Nevada
—Humboldt, towns in Illinois, Iowa, Kansas, Minnesota, South Dakota, Tennessee, and Saskatchewan, Canada
—Humboldt Bay, northern New Guinea
—Humboldt Glacier, Greenland
—Humboldt State Redwood Park, California
—Humboldt Mountains, China
—Humboldt Peaks in Colorado and Venezuela
—Humboldt River, Nevada
—Humboldt Current, Pacific Ocean

More important to him than all the honors was the fact that the people were finding great value in his last and, in his mind, most important writings. The already published volumes of *Cosmos* were selling well, in the thousands.

He shook himself impatiently from his reverie at the thought of the popularity of *Cosmos*. The time of quietude and sad contemplation after the shadow of death across his vision was past. Fresh life, fresh resolve poured into him. He was a fool, he told himself, to be sitting here pondering death and reviewing the past. There was still the future. He had given up travel to write *Cosmos*. He had surrendered the past years to hard work when he could have been resting on his laurels. Now was not the time to quit, not at this late stage in the work. The world must have all of the *Cosmos.* After he had finished with it, then perhaps he would think of death.

He stood up slowly. He put his hands on his hips and arched his back, sighing a little. He would start again on Volume Five this evening. He touched a sheaf of papers on the desk. All his notes for the next chapters were in order, ready and waiting for him.

He walked to the door. He would rest a little before the night's work. The cool air in the adjoining room touched him. He shivered slightly. He had never liked the cold. He smiled a little in anticipation. Perhaps when he lay down in the bedroom he would fall asleep. And then perhaps he would dream again—as he had so often in the past months—of South America. He would find himself young again and with Aimé, perhaps on the Orinoco, perhaps laughing atop the Raudal de los Gauhibos in the rainbow mist hanging against the yellow sunlight, or perhaps moving slowly, lazily, over the tawny waters of the Magdalena down to Hondo. Then he would be warm again.

He entered his bedroom, closing the door behind him. The firelight played softly on the notes of a book that would never be complete. The rooms were very quiet and lonely.

ALEXANDER VON HUMBOLDT
September 14, 1769—May 6, 1859.